John Jean

Families Matter!

Bob Ivey

the.Iveys@gte.net
214.668.2980

BOILING THE FROG

Boiling *the* Frog

Crises in the American first Family

by Dick Ivey, Ph.D.

Published by Intrepid Press

Printed in the United States of America

Library of Congress Cataloging in Publication Data

Ivey, Dick.

      Boiling the Frog: Crises in the American First Family / by Dick Ivey

ISBN 0-9670491-0-5

Book design by Sean Walker

Preface

"Nothing happens unless first a dream."
CARL SANDBURG

I've been told you can't put a live frog in hot water and keep it from jumping out of the pot. On the other hand, if you put a frog in cold water and gradually raise the temperature, you can boil the frog without it ever realizing the water has gotten hot. Apparently, something in the frog's nerve endings desensitizes it to gradual increases in temperature so that it can literally be boiled without knowing it.

Over the years various crises regarding the family have heated the world until it is at the boiling point. Because many of the crises we find ourselves in came about as gradually and unobtrusively as boiling water on a kitchen range, we are often desensitized to the impact they have on our lives, and on the lives of our loved ones.

In this novel the names of real people are intertwined with people of my imagination. There is no intent to suggest that the events of this book have happened, or will happen, to the real people whose names are included. However, I do hope that some or all of the real people who appear in this story will become part of the solutions it begs....and that there will be lots more just like them.

On the other hand, the dream I refer to is crystal clear. I can only hope that the outcomes projected here that can affect American families for the better will be historical fact when the year two thousand thirteen actually arrives. Indeed, it is my passion that the outcomes stated herein are far more conservative than the realities that will emerge.

Unless, and until, we address the issues you will encounter in this story our society will continue to raise the temperature in our homes a degree at a time until *we boil the frog*.

Acknowledgments

"If you want to succeed you should strike out on new paths
rather than travel the worn paths of accepted success."
JOHN D. ROCKEFELLER, SR.

"We need men who can dream things that never were."
JOHN F. KENNEDY

I am deeply indebted to the following people who have helped shape the dream that takes form in this book:

*My parents, **Bates and Lucy Ivey**, who have always told me
I could even when I thought I couldn't.*

***Raleigh Holt**, my long deceased high school track coach, who would not let me
learn to practice the ugly art of quitting just because the going was tough.*

***Leon Marsh**, my major professor in graduate school, and his wife Ruth, who
inspired me to persevere educationally and to pursue individual paths many
people are afraid to imagine or take.*

*Dear friends and gifts from God, **John C. and Helen Treadaway**,
from whom I have learned to never, never, never, never give up or give in.*

*To the charter members of the Executive Committee of KenField Institute—
Stan Craig, Doug Dillard, David Humphrey, Paul Royal and
Barry Brelsford. Gents, it is to be.*

*To **Rocko and Shel Crawford**, who showed us all the way to go.*

To C.C. Risenhoover, who combed this manuscript with a fine toothed comb for order, syntax, grammar and punctuation, and who shares the dream.

To Barry Robert Brelsford who provided the details of SEAL training, armaments and procedures, and whose friendship I prize.

To Ken Pepper, Ph.D., my mentor, my counselor, my friend. He died with his "things to do before I die" list in his pocket, doing something wild and wonderful—canoeing. He always saw through my facáde and called me on my posturing and was one of the key instruments in helping the redhead and me make our house a home. Gone too soon. The Ken of KenField.

To Don Lansing, Al Ameskamp, Ray Kinsella, Kevin Kostner, James Earl Jones and thousands of others who keep coming to the small farm near Dyersville, Iowa, where Don and Al provided the setting for the memorable nineteen eighty-nine film Field of Dreams.

"Build it and they will come."

"Go the distance."

"Ease his pain."

This memorable film and the great closing words from James Earl Jones helped us hold onto the dream during some of the toughest years of waiting for it to take shape.

"People will come, Ray.

They'll come to Iowa for reasons they can't fathom.

They'll arrive at your door, innocent as children, longing for the past...

it will be as if they dipped themselves in magic waters."

This is the Field of KenField Institute, and is a constant and continuing reminder of our need to stay the course...to build it and they will come.

To our own J. Barresford Tipton, may his generosity make the dream a reality.

And, finally, to my bride, Barbara, the redhead in my life, with whom the dream that has spawned this fiction has had its birth pains, adolescence and budding maturity—and with whom I expect to observe this dream grow old and pass to those who will follow and whose names I do not yet know.

Prologue

The story you are about to read had its beginnings in a kitchen conversation with the gorgeous redhead, my bride, Barbara. While watching the Oprah Winfrey show one afternoon, she was impressed by Oprah's commitment to showcase authors who write pro-family materials.

I shared our conversation with my good friend Doug Dillard, who suggested I use the KenField dream and write it as a novel in which our dreams for healthier families have already come to pass.

Sandwiched between the story line and dream is a fictional conversation in two thousand thirteen between the seventy-three-year-old man I will be and my eldest grandson Ryan.

I can but hope that the real story in this book is prophetic.

Contents

The End of the Beginning

"Never tell a young person that something cannot be done. God may have been waiting for centuries for somebody ignorant enough of the impossible to do that very thing."

DR. J. A. HOLMES

"Pop, have you got a minute?" my grandson Ryan asked.

It matters not how often one of my grandchildren asks that question. Even if I am busy, I take the time, whether they request a minute, hour, day or week. It pleases me to be there for them.

We have six grandchildren—five nearly grown young men and a lovely blue-eyed blonde who reminds me somewhat of Sheldie Crawford. Believe me when I say that she always has been able to get what she wanted from her grandpop—and always will.

Of course, I would not trade the five guys for anything either.

I am seventy-three years old, married to my best friend and living in the most idyllic setting I can imagine—surrounded by my family. For almost twenty years I have been living my long-time dream of helping families gain more and better skills in being husbands, wives and parents.

Since our three grown children have in-laws who want the kids and grandchildren to be at their homes on Christmas day, my bride and I usually schedule a weekend just prior to, or just after December twenty-fifth, to gather them at the most convenient common home.

1

Since moving to the ranch in East Texas, we most often gather there—which is where we are when Ryan, my eldest grandson, requested a minute.

Ryan's a little hard to believe at times, but in a good sense. For example, it is hard to believe that this big hulk is the tiny creature I cradled back on December nineteen of nineteen ninety-three when his daddy announced, "It's a boy!"

I remember the day just like it was yesterday, which, I guess, reinforces the idea that old codgers like me tend to live within our ancient memories. The redhead and I were at our daughter's home celebrating her graduation from college when we got the call from our son that this man-child now before me was on the way.

What a memorable evening—the joy of celebrating our daughter's completion of a major accomplishment in her life and learning that our first grandchild was on the way. Our daughter shared in the joy and insisted that we leave the party early. She was as excited about being an aunt as we were about being grandparents.

So off we went—driving two hundred and fifty miles and enjoying the anticipation all the way. We arrived at the hospital parking lot at one-thirty in the morning and rushed into the family waiting room.

We could have taken our time. Ryan was not born until three forty-five a.m. None of us knew if this child was going to be boy, girl or frog. His parents had elected not to know his gender before he was born. I will never forget that silly grin on our number one son's face when he made the announcement and we were all invited into the birthing suite to hold the minutes-old critter.

There is nothing like a first grandchild. For that matter, there is nothing like any grandchild. You get to spoil them, enjoy them and then send them home. It is a way of getting even with your kids for some of the misery they caused you.

That reminds me of a friend of mine, Jack Clator, who was hurrying to take his grandchildren home on a Sunday afternoon and said to his wife, "Boy, I can't wait to get back to wondering what these kids are doing instead of knowing for sure."

There has been lots of water under the bridge since that day nearly twenty years ago. I sometimes wonder where the time has gone. This all flashed through my mind as I looked up at my handsome grandson—ice blue eyes, a shock of blond hair, six-foot, three inches tall and two hundred muscular pounds. And, I am glad he had interrupted my late afternoon reverie on the sweeping back porch of our home, which is my favorite spot for just thinking and enjoying.

I've been sitting in this same old butt-wallowed-out rocking chair for more years than I care to admit, watching the end of days go slowly into night. The view of the sunset across the lake always gives me a sense of calm and gratitude for all that life has brought me. Watching day give way to night is a good time for me.

"Sure, buddy," I told my grandson. "Come, sit. What's up?"

"Pop, I need somebody to talk to who's not as emotionally involved as my mom and dad," he says. "Every time I ask either one of them, it gets to be a marathon conversation that goes nowhere."

"Whoa, slow down a bit and let me catch up. What are you talking about?"

"Sorry to put this on you," he said. "But I just don't know what to do."

"Well, sit down and tell me about it. How can I help?

I wish I could just flop down over the side of a chair the way he does. He does not have a clue about the little things he takes for granted—like getting up or sitting down without grunting and groaning.

"Okay, here's the deal," he says. "I'll be a junior this fall and I don't have the foggiest idea about what I'm going to do when I get out of college. I need to talk to someone who doesn't get agitated when I talk about being a rodeo cowboy, moving to Hollywood to produce films or going to Alaska to fish for salmon. It's not as if I really think I'll do those things, but what if I do? The truth of the matter is that I'm not really juiced about anything right now."

3

Juiced, I thought. Must be a new adolescent term.

"Bud, I'm..."

He held up a hand and stopped me. "Wait a minute, Pop, I'm not through yet. What I really want to know is about you. How did you get the fire in your belly for the work you do at KenField?"

He has always been like that. I do not know how he can get so many words out of his mouth in one breath. When he pauses, I am never sure whether he is ready for some input or just stoking up for another round. The kid started talking a blue streak when he was a year old and has not stopped since.

As for the KenField Institute (KFI) to which he referred, it is an organization his Grammy and I founded back in nineteen eighty-eight. It was named for Ken Pepper, founder of the Pastoral Counseling and Education Center in Dallas—who died at age seventy-one in a freak canoeing accident—and the nineteen eighty nine hit movie, *Field of Dreams.* "If you build it, he will come" kept us focused on the dream many years before it was finally realized.

The purpose of KFI is to establish and promote healthy family life practices on a national scale. It has been the passion and life work of my redheaded bride and me for more than twenty-five years.

Ryan continued, "Have you always wanted to do that? The KenField thing, I mean. I know you've done lots of other stuff, but ever since I can remember, you've really been hyped on your KenField work. I thought by now you and Grammy would have retired and just be enjoying your later years. Why are you still working? What gives you your drive and fire. And how can I get some of it for me?"

I thought, *later years,* my foot. I can still take you out, kid. Funny how I always think there is a twenty-year-old running around inside me. I still have days when I get up in the morning, look in the mirror and wonder what my dad is doing at our house.

I raised my hand this time and he said, "Huh?"

"Is it my turn yet?" I asked.

He smiled. And he has a dandy. His smile, along with the good looks, is why he always has a pretty young woman around. In fact, I had wondered why he had not brought one with him this particular weekend? He made a fist and cuffed me on the shoulder.

"C'mon, Pop, I'm serious. I don't want to just let my life leak out one day at a time. I really want some of that fire you and Grammy have for what you do. How'd you get it?"

"There isn't a simple answer to that question, Ryan, but I'll take a swing at it. And you can interrupt any time you want…as if I have to give you that option."

He laughed, and I continued, "I'm glad you're stretching your imagination, glad you're trying to find out where your own passion lies. If you were to go off to ride wild horses or to catch fish in Alaska, I would worry about you. But, I want you to go where your heart takes you. Of course, if you go to Hollywood and get in the film business, then I'll join your mom and dad and be more than just worried about you."

He laughed again, a soft, easy laugh that is much like his father's— open, but with a deep reserve where only he can go. Was it Yogi or Casey who said, "Déjà vu all over again?" Me, too.

"Tell me, buddy," I asked, "what are you doing to get a sense of direction and purpose for your life?"

He grinned and said, "Well, so far this is it, but that's why I'm asking you. I don't know anybody on the planet who loves what they do more than you and Grammy."

"I'll get to that in a minute," I said, "but indulge the old man a moment. What would you do with your life if you were independently wealthy and could do anything you wanted?"

There was a long pause and for a moment I thought he was ignoring me. But then I noted the faraway look in his eyes that told me there was some serious number crunching going on in his fertile young mind.

"Pop, I started to say something stupid like 'sleep until noon every day.' Or, 'play golf until I get good enough to go on tour.' Or, 'move to the beach and become a beach bum'. But this is serious, so I won't give you some trite answer. I like to do lots of stuff, but nothing that I'd want to do forever. I'd still like to find something I could really feel pumped about all the time. Isn't there something I can do to find that zing?"

"Let me try it another way," I said. "Let's look at things you do well. Give me a list of the top three things you like to do...in school, sports or just for fun."

"Hmmm, let's see. I like history, computer science and verbal courses such as speech...drama, debate and persuasion...stuff like that. I like rugby, golf and basketball, but I don't see myself playing rugby after I get out of school. I watch Dad hobble around and I don't want to get like that."

"Just for fun, I like to watch movies. I like coming out here...and I really like to fish. How does that help?"

I laughed and replied, "My guess, my all-time favorite number one grandson, is that your passion...or calling...or zinger for living is embedded in there somewhere. Your job it to polish those skills and interests that you like today. Then when your special task is revealed to you, it will take advantage of the gifts you have been given and the tools you've honed sharp.

"If you like history, computer science and communication, learn all you can about the period of history that you love best. Become proficient in computer science, either as an application specialist or a techie...whatever floats your boat."

He paused reflectively and said, "No techie stuff for me, Pop. I don't care how the stuff works. I just like making the stuff sizzle that's out there. I might want to create software sometime, but that isn't my most favorite thing to do."

"Okay, no techie stuff," I said, " but I'd sure learn how the hardware works and how to use the Internet and Intranet technologies with all the interactive, artificial intelligence and virtual reality stuff as well as more traditional software applications.

"As for the communication stuff, there's a world of things you can do if you can speak before groups, make oral presentations in business, negotiate, bargain, persuade, debate. Learn those skills. They travel well. Lots of businesses need people who do that competently. Shoot, that's how I made my living most of my life before KenField...persuading somebody or selling something."

There was that big hand again. He stopped me in midstream and there was no smile on his face. I thought I might have offended him, but after hearing what came out of his mouth you could have knocked me over with a feather. "Pop, what I really want to know is how you got your passion and whether you could use a kid like me? Maybe if I just worked with you a while, some of your passion might just rub off on me."

It was my turn to be quiet and reflective. Suddenly a lump appeared in my throat and my eyes started to leak. My dream and Barbara's had been for all our children and grandchildren to have an interest in working with us at KenField. Sometimes I have had to bite my tongue just to keep from being too persuasive with them—because as much as I want them to be with us, I have also wanted them to be their own persons and choose their own way. I readily admit, however, that I have been very grateful for those who do work with us.

Now, at the threshold of another generation, it seemed that another of our own wanted to stick his toe in the same water we had found so refreshing.

It was all I could do to keep from jumping up and down and shouting, but I did not want to frighten him away. I wanted him to get a good taste of what we were doing. Then he would know if he wanted to pursue it as his life's work. After all, I remembered how difficult it had always been for me to be passionate about another man's dream—and I certainly didn't want to unduly influence this young dreamer who was my grandson, nor did I want to squash his search before it reached home.

"Grab a coat, let's go for a walk," I said.

We ambled slowly down toward the manicured edge of the fifty-five acre lake on the west side of our home. I hooked my hand in his arm

7

and we just enjoyed each other's company in silence.

Moments later I broke the silence. "The answer to your second question is easy. As long as I have something to do, there will always be a place for bright young men like you. How would you like to do a summer internship with us...then tell me what you think?"

His body language gave me an exuberant affirmative answer. He picked me up in a bear hug and scared every creature within fifty miles with a "Wahoo!"

Laughing, I said, "Put me down, Ryan. You don't know your own strength."

When my feet were on the ground again, I said, "There are some caveats that go with the work. I won't make work for you. The job will be real. You'll be an important cog in our machine. You can't work directly for me or for anyone in our family. You can be fired if you don't perform. And, I'll pay you fairly for your work. You'll even have to negotiate your salary. However, I'll give you some pointers on that if you like.

"Now do you still want to come play at our party?"

"Absolutely," he said, "and I'll take all the help I can get."

By now we had wandered past the pecan orchard and were almost to the concrete picnic table—the one the cows kept pushing over when we let them graze under the trees during the spring and summer before the nuts were on the ground. We always came through and scattered the manure after it dried so we would not have to warn anyone, "Don't cut your foot."

The cows had been gone a while so there was no danger of getting an unwanted mess on our boots, but the concrete table and benches were still overturned by the last old mossy backed cow that had an itch she could not scratch any place else.

Without a word, we grabbed opposite sides of the table's top, replaced it on the pedestal and righted the three concrete benches. I wiped off a spot on one of the benches and sat down. Ryan just plopped down, mindless of any dirt that might be on his bench.

"I guess I have been avoiding your other question, Mr. Ryan King," I said, chuckling. We had been calling him The Ryan King ever since he was a little tyke. When he was a toddler his lovely mom could keep him occupied—and to give herself a little rest—by plugging in a video. First, *Barney*, then *The Jungle Book*, then *The Lion King* and a shelf full of others that we have put away for our great grandchildren. Ryan watched *The Lion King* over and over until all the grownups around him could repeat the dialogue verbatim. And so, he became affectionately known as The Ryan King.

"But the answer is not an easy one," I continued, "and I don't want to bore you with the details, so I have been thinking about my words carefully.

"I doubt that you've read the first book I wrote back in the seventies when your dad was just a kid. It was a story of the tragedy that occurred in our home when I was divorced from your grandmother Kaye. The title is *My Marriage Was Lousy and My Divorce Ain't So Hot!* It's tongue-in-cheek, but serious, because it deals with the pain of divorce for people who have children.

"As we moved farther and farther away from the time of our divorce, I kept wondering how a smart-rat like your old Pop could have screwed up his marriage as badly as he did. It didn't seem fair. There we were, pretty smart people, but without the slightest idea about how to go about being husband and wife or parents.

"The more I thought about it, the more angry I became that there wasn't anyone out there with help available for folks like us and for future generations.

"My purpose in writing the book was to first get my own head on straight...and to tell other people not to travel the road I had taken. I was so banged up mentally that I needed some emotional surgery. We didn't publish the book until late in the nineties, but by then the dream and the passion you have asked me about were already old.

"Over time the idea for KenField kept growing...like dandelions in the pavement or Johnson grass in the pasture. Your grandmother, Barbara, and I figured there was something we could do to keep our children and grandchildren from failing as spouses and parents. The thought wouldn't go away.

"In the late eighties the idea came to us that there ought to an independent, permanently endowed, private agency to examine all the causes of family failure and work on ways to stop the erosion for future generations. We looked for such an agency or organization with whom to associate ourselves, but it became clear that there wasn't anything like that in existence. That's when KenField was born."

As I talked the sun began to rest on the far side of the lake. Its shimmering rays passed through the small trees on the postage stamp island in the middle of the lake and made a picture perfect impression memory. The lake was mirror-still and everything around us was quiet—other than the scuffing sounds we made when we moved. I suggested we start back toward the house where Grammy would have dinner on for us.

Grammy, I thought. That's what the kids had called my gorgeous redhead, Barbara, since Ryan was born. That had gotten me to doing it, too, along with the grandkids. Thoughts of Barbara always melted me. She's my best friend and partner and, despite the years, more beautiful now than the day I married her—though that hardly seems possible.

We had traveled only a short distance when we heard the dinner gong ring. By the time we walked the half-mile back to the house it would be time to wash up.

I took Ryan's arm again and said, "No matter what happened all those years, no matter how I made a living, the thought of helping families learn what I didn't know as a young husband and father just wouldn't go away.

"Lots of folks thought I was crazy. And I was beginning to feel that way, too, but I couldn't get it out of my system. We worked for years to find private funding for our dream, but it was the dramatic events that occurred when you were about eight or nine years old to really set this dream in motion and put us where we are today.

"It began with the *Wake-Up Call to America* speech that President and Mrs. Crawford made to the country shortly after the tragedy in the White House back in two thousand two."

I interrupted myself by patting him on the stomach, "I'll continue the story later, if you really want to hear it. Of course, it's not just a make-believe story like a drama played out on television or in the movies. It's real life history, what's known and isn't known. And, it catapulted us right into the realization of our dream."

Tragedy in the White House

"As important as your obligations as a doctor, lawyer or business leader will be, you are a human being first, and those human connections—with spouses, with children, with friends— are the most important investments you will ever make. At the end of your life, you will never regret not having passed one more test, not winning one more verdict, or not closing one more deal. You will regret time not spent with a husband, a child, a friend, or a parent. Our success as a society depends not on what happens in the White House, but on what happens in your house."

BARBARA BUSH, *Wellesley College Commencement Address, 1990*

After dinner Ryan and I went down to my study. Fifteen years ago, this old house was our dream. I remember my bride's *dream board* of pictures and photographs of her ideal home. This is it. Funny how a few years and the increasing impact of arthritic knees—inherited and then cultivated by all the years of running and playing ball—have colored what the ideal house would look like for us today. There would not be stairs to climb.

I have always loved my study, but now hate going up and down the stairs that lead to it. We left the dining room and made our way carefully, step by step, down the stairs to the expanse of glass that looks out over the lake in our front yard and gives us an unobstructed view of lots of Georgia O'Keefe sunsets.

Behind the glass, raised mahogany panels cover the other three walls of my refuge here at the ranch. I have sat in the room's overstuffed chairs for countless hours and read thousands of pages. I have warmed myself in front of the cozy fireplace to the left of the large, old, simple

13

cherry desk that I have had for all these years. It sets opposite the glass wall and stands guard over some of my greatest treasures—medals, plaques, photographs, and a collection of bronzed headlines from April twenty-third in the year two thousand and two.

The framed headlines on the wall behind my desk say it all: *Washington Post*, *New York Times*, *Chicago Tribune*, *Los Angeles Times*, and *Dallas Morning News* scream angry black ink words that should have made even the tabloids blush—and were about as accurate.

"I have two collections now," I told Ryan. "The ones from that fateful fall day in Dallas in nineteen sixty-three when John Kennedy was killed have been lying in the bottom of a drawer for more than fifty years. They're faded and yellow. As you can see, I've framed the new ones, because they mark the beginning of the new day in our nation. It's tragic that it took something of this magnitude to get us all to wake up. And, only the events that followed really made a difference."

The headlines beg for an explanation.

First Lady Shel Crawford Dead
First Lady ODs
Shel Crawford Critical After Overdose
First Lady Apparent Suicide–Note Found
First Brat Pregnant
President Finds Wife Comatose in Lincoln Bedroom
Suicide Note Shocks Nation
Shelden Crawford Pregnant at 14

I knew the story—all of it. And, to the best of my ability, I began to tell it to my grandson.

Shel Crawford had not been a happy woman for several years. Despite her high social upbringing, a distinguished career in academia and a story book romance with a young Navy SEAL war hero who became President, she was a lonely woman. Despite two gorgeous children and her place as the First Lady of the land, she was driven by the sham of her own home and family.

•••

Shel had not been seen all day. No one remembered seeing her leave the White House. Her Secret Service detail had not been alerted that she planned an off campus trip. None of the staff recalled seeing her during the day.

After breakfast her husband, the President, had gone to the Oval Office. Her children, Chip and Sheldie, went to school.

Rockland Hamilton Crawford, Jr. was *Chip* to everyone who knew him. He was truly a chip off the old Rock. He was a lot like his daddy—ruggedly handsome, piercing ice blue eyes and a forever-tan complexion. Though only seventeen, not so much as a pimple had marked his unblemished face. The only physical characteristic inherited from his mother was a thick mane of blond hair. He would become a high school *Parade* All-America football player despite playing in a private school league for Alexander Hamilton Prep School in the Washington suburb of McLean, Virginia.

Shelden "Sheldie" Crawford, named for her mother Shelby Denise—with no middle name of her own—was individualistic to a fault. She was brash and bold, an adventurer from the time she was a baby. Her tomboy years, however, were short-lived. By age twelve she had the body of a grown woman. And, at fourteen, she was every young man's fantasy and parents' nightmare.

A near perfect female specimen at this young age, Sheldie was five feet seven inches tall and weighed one hundred eighteen pounds. She had luxurious auburn hair, bright green eyes, long legs, a dirt dauber waist and a bust-line that turned heads. When all dressed up, she looked as if she had stepped off the cover of a fashion magazine. Her one concession to convention was simple, but artistic make-up and hair styling. She also avoided the teen fads of pierced body parts, including her ears.

And yet, she always pushed the envelope as far as it would go.

When convention dictated that she wear a proper uniform or dress clothes to the exclusive girls' academy where she was an eighth grader, she often wore baggy sweat clothes. She dared the headmaster to send her home and won. Defiantly, she told her mother she would wear what she chose to wear.

But, even under a baggy outfit, Sheldie could not hide the sexual energy that she neither understood nor made any effort to conceal. Fortunately or unfortunately, her typical outfits also hid her biggest secret from everyone else.

•••

Shelby Denise Crawford, *Shel,* the only child of the historic Boston Haverfords, a Ph.D. from Massachusetts Institute of Technology and wife of the President of the United States, was finally alone. The staff was busy clearing the kitchen of the breakfast dishes and she was able to sneak into the Lincoln bedroom without being seen. Shel was fairly certain that she would not be disturbed until she had finished what she intended to do. She had everything she needed and, in the back of the cavernous closet with the door shut, she was as secluded as she could get and still be in the White House.

What a joke this place was, she thought. And what a joke her family was. This was just the last straw. Even if she was able to go on with the charade, enough was enough. This thing with Shelden was more than she could handle. She was tired. And, stopping her world was easier to contemplate than going on.

She made a nest of throw pillows in a corner and surveyed her tools: a yellow legal pad and a broad tipped black felt pen, the small ice bucket that was the first piece of silver she had bought right after she and Rocko were married when he was two years out of Annapolis. Filling it with ice without attracting the kitchen staff had been tricky, but she had managed. The one and a half liter bottle of hundred proof vodka was tucked in the bottom of the beach tote that contained her other things.

16

She smiled, recalling her mother's humorous advice almost every time she left their home when she was younger: "Make sure you wear clean underwear when you go out, you never know if you might have an accident and wind up in the hospital."

Well, this isn't exactly going out in the classic sense, she thought. *But then, maybe it is.*

Shel was not sure why, but she had showered after the kids left for school. She had also put on her finest sheer black lace silk bikini panties from Victoria's Secret. *Maybe I can't ignore mother's advice*, she thought, smiling grimly.

In the bottom of the beach tote were the three other key ingredients— a half empty bottle of Percodan, a highball glass and ten sleeping pills. The sleeping pills were old. The label was so smudged she could not read the prescription name. Dr. James Harris had prescribed them for her during Rocko's Strike Force mission to rescue the Vice President.

Unable to sleep for days on end, Shel finally succumbed to the prescription. Her life-long aversion to medication had been overcome by sheer exhaustion. She had taken them four nights before she became afraid of the loss of control they created in her. She had slept twelve to fourteen hours at a stretch whenever she took only one of them.

Settling down in her nest, Shelby Denise Crawford filled the crystal glass she had spirited from the private bar in the bedroom she shared with Rocko. She liked the sound the small ice cubes made in the bottom of the glass. She twisted the cap off the vodka bottle, raised it to her lips and drank. Then she filled the glass to the top.

She had refused to admit, even to herself, that she had become a closet alcoholic. Yet, any day she did not have an outside schedule, she was drinking before the kids cleared the driveway on their way to school. She had learned to hide the side effects and the smell—at least she thought she had—and had become increasingly less interested in even her most prized projects. There were just too many excuses she could use, and did.

Today I think I'll admit I'm an alcoholic, she thought. *It's no big deal. Besides, who cares? I like this stuff. Anyway, it doesn't matter any more. I can't take it, not another day.*

By then the glass was empty and she had poured another. She settled down, took the yellow pad and pen and began to write.

Dear Chipper,

It is only because of my fierce love for you that I have not done this years ago. You are my pride and joy. If I could have special ordered you, I would not have changed a thing. You are so strong, tall and handsome. Smart, too. When you digest the contents of this note, as you will, please read all the lines and between the lines to know that this is not about you. It is not in any way about you.

The pain of the lie that I live with your father is just too much. Maybe if this thing with Sheldie hadn't gotten in the way, and you will learn about it soon enough, I could go on pretending, but now I don't have any more fight in me. I just want it to all go away. And since it won't, I am doing the only other thing I can think to do. I'm going away.

I love you, my darling child. I regret the pain and anger that my actions today will cause you. This is not about you. Make that a mantra for yourself as you recover from this day. You can and must go on. Graduate, get your college degrees and learn from our mistakes as you create your own family. Take good care of your wife, whoever she may be. Learn about commitment and the difference between your hormones and feelings and real love. Love is not about how you feel, it's about how you behave. Do better than your dad and I have. I wish I could be there when you meet and marry her.

Love,

Mom

She turned the page and began to write again.

18

Rocko,

You bastard. I don't know when I began to hate you, but ever since I found that first smudge of lipstick on your shirt collar right after we were married, I should have known that you would never have any loyalty to me. I've lost count of the rumors and stopped chasing about to find out who you are bedding these days. I'm not sure that even being the Big Boss has made any difference.

God, how I loved you. I pretended so many times that I was just being paranoid, but deep down I knew. I could smell them on you and their perfume lingered to mock me when you came home. Oh, I know you thought you were being so clever and cautious, but let me tell you, you low life scum, I always knew. I wish I'd had enough courage to face you down about this years ago before it got so far out of hand.

I pretended to be your loving wife to the world outside. I even pretended sex with you was wonderful and, admittedly, sometimes it was. But deep down, I have been miserable with you for nearly seventeen years.

Maybe, just maybe, if I hadn't intercepted a call on Sheldie's phone yesterday, I could have continued to keep up appearances so your precious political career could go on presenting the lie as the truth, but no more. Others may call you warrior, President and war hero, but not me. You're a two-faced philandering dog in heat.

My only regret, except for Chip, is that I won't be here tomorrow when you have to begin explaining to the world why your trophy wife committed suicide. I hope you squirm and sweat and get everything you have coming. I really hate you. I hope you rot in hell.

By the time you get this you will have official confirmation that your precious daughter, for whom you set such a wonderful example, is pregnant. God knows who the father is, but she is in week twenty-five to twenty-seven of having your first grandchild—and just now getting confirmation from a doctor.

She hasn't even told me. If I hadn't gone by her room and answered her phone yesterday, I would not know about her going to the public health clinic on her own and somehow managing to get them to confirm her fears without involving us. When I identified myself as Shel, I suppose the young doctor on the other end of the line thought I was Sheldie. By the time I had recovered from the shock of hearing that he was from the public health clinic, I had already heard the news. She is pregnant. I poked around in her room and found a home pregnancy test kit hidden in the back of her underwear drawer. The test strip was still there, wrapped in a scarf, blue as could be. Getting to the bottom of that ought to give you a convenient target for your self-righteous indignation.

My guess is that you won't take any responsibility for this fiasco either. Either way, you are going to have to go this one alone.

I can't bear to bring more shame on my parents than we already have. I know this is going to hurt them, but I just can't abide you another day. I don't care what sort of formal event you decide to stage, but when it is all over I just want to be cremated and taken home. I'd like for my dad to take me out on the big sailboat (whose name I can never remember) and scatter me over the bay at Martha's Vineyard. That's the last place I really remember being happy, so I'd like to stay there. And, besides, I don't want some monument as a grim reminder to my children of what you have driven me to do.

If I am lucky, nobody will find me before the Percodan, sleeping pills and some elegant vodka have done their magic. In fact, it won't bother me if I am not found for a day or so.

So long, sucker. I can only hope this hurts you as much as you have hurt me.

She had to start over several times, and was surrounded with crumpled pieces of yellow pad paper, before being satisfied that she had fully expressed her pent-up anger.

Finally, My Dear Sheldie:
It wasn't my intention to invade your privacy when I answered

your phone yesterday, but I did. Your phone was ringing when I came past your room, and without thinking about it I just answered it. The doctor thought I was you and read me the results of your test. You are pregnant and have been for several months. When he hung up I searched your room and found your home pregnancy test kit. I can only presume that you managed to get to the public health clinic in some fashion and hide your identity. I wish I could hear how you managed that trick. I can't imagine how you have hidden this from us all these months. You must not have gained any weight at all.

I have so many questions, but now will never know the answers. I wish I knew the father of the baby you are carrying. I wish I knew when you managed to find the time and place to get pregnant. I wish I had known about this before you were five to seven months pregnant. I don't know what the final choice might have been, but having options would have at least been preferable.

I won't dwell on it, but if you have the baby, I wish I were going to be here to hold it. Dear God, you are just a baby and are having a baby. I'm sorry I wasn't a better mother.

I am so tired of your father's treatment of me, and so embarrassed about it. I can't live this way any more. I hope you survive this and can overcome it, but I can't worry about that any more.

I don't understand you, but someday I hope you will understand that I do love you.
Mommy

Tears streaming down her face, she began writing a note to her parents.

Daddy and Mum:
Please forgive me. I love you all so much. I just can't take the subterfuge anymore. Please insure that they cremate me and then bury me at sea in MV. Good-bye. I have sent you a revised copy of my will. I am leaving everything to Chip and Sheldie, but I am counting on you to

see to the trustees and trust funds. Please take care of them.
Shelly

She took a fresh sheet and penned the following:

Mavis, please send this note unopened to Malcolm Willingham at the
Washington Post.
Shel

The First Lady tore off the pages and folded them neatly in half. There was a manila envelope in the beach tote that she had addressed to Mavis Cortland, her appointment secretary. She sealed the envelope and attached the note to Mavis with a paper clip.

The next three minutes were the most difficult. She hit her fifth glass of vodka with her knee as she stood. It spilled on the closet floor and soaked into the carpet. She tiptoed to the door of the bedroom and listened intently until all noise died in the hallway outside. She opened the door a crack and peered into the empty hallway, then walked across the hallway and placed the envelope on the lamp table against the opposite wall. She frequently left messages on the table for delivery to Mavis and was sure it would find its way to her. The last thing she wanted was for Rocko to find the note and destroy it.

She returned to the safety of the closet, gathered the crumpled pieces of yellow paper, placed them behind a box on the top shelf of the closet and moved a throw pillow to cover the spilled drink. Now for the big event—the final event. She sat, opened each bottle of pills and dumped them on the floor. There were twenty-one. She put a Percodan in her mouth, then a sleeping pill and took a swallow of vodka.

After swallowing five pills, she decided to see how many she could take at one time. She was able to swallow three at one time. After two more glasses of vodka all the pills were gone.

Shel slid down to a reclining position and refilled her glass one more time. Settling back, she drank slowly. The bottle was nearly empty.

At first she slept, then fell into an unconscious state. Her breathing slowed perceptibly, an involuntary shudder spilled the remaining liquid from the glass and then the closet was silent and still. When blackness enveloped her the Piaget watch on her wrist read three forty-seven p.m.

At day's end the children ate alone, as they frequently did when their parents were busy with the business of being President and First Lady. Neither the children nor the staff was immediately concerned that Shel Crawford was not there for dinner.

At six fifteen p.m. the President returned to his third floor residence at the White House and greeted his children. It was early for him. Chip was busy on a school project and Shelden was buried under a Walkman—lost somewhere in a hard rock classic of unknown origin or destination. Rocko didn't notice the tears on the face of his baby girl. He grabbed a snack from the kitchen and retired to his study.

Just before seven o'clock Mavis Cortland called for Shel. Chip answered the phone and told her that he had not seen her since getting home. He suggested that maybe his dad would know his mother's whereabouts and transferred the call into the study.

"Mr. President, I am concerned about Shel," Cortland said. "She sent me a package to be delivered to Malcolm over at the *Post*. And Malcolm called insisting that he see Mrs. Crawford or talk to you. I've tried to put him off until tomorrow. And, I apologize for bothering you.

"He won't go away. He's adamant that he speaks to one of you, or he's going to come over there to make a scene now. I don't know what that means, but I thought you would want to know."

Crawford asked if Malcolm was still on the line, was informed that he was and said, "Put him through, Mavis. I don't know where Shel is at the moment, but let's see what has the fourth estate so up in arms at this hour of the evening. We wouldn't want to miss anything that might be in the headlines tomorrow, would we?"

Mavis would, of course, remember that haunting line for years to come. Crawford did not comprehend how prophetic his words were about to become. She transferred the call and dropped off the line.

The senior political correspondent for the *Post*, long-time friend of the Crawfords but consummate journalist, came on the line with the question, "Mr. President, do you know where your wife is?" The tension in his voice was unmistakable—none of the usual pleasantries.

"No, Mal, why do you ask? Is there a problem?"

"I'm afraid something awful has happened to Shelly." Willingham was one of the few Washington insiders who called the First Lady *Shelly*, the pet name given her by her father.

"Tell me what's going on, Mal?"

"Mr. President, I have reason to believe that your wife is missing and in grave danger. I was hoping she was home with you. Please see if you can locate her. And, if you will permit an intrusion at this hour, I want to come see you with the package she sent to me today by Mavis. Check her schedule and see if anyone knows where she is. I'll be there in thirty minutes."

After hanging up the phone, Crawford called Mavis back and asked her if she knew anything about Shel's schedule for the day, or about the package she had delivered to Willingham. Mavis told him she had no outside schedule for the First Lady for the day and had not examined the contents of the package. She told him it was not likely that her boss had slipped away without her attending Secret Service escort, though it had happened a time or two in the past. She promised to check further and call back.

Crawford was more irritated than worried, but he got up and went to check with the kids to see if they knew the whereabouts of their mother. Chip said he had no clue. He had not seen her since breakfast that morning.

Shelden was still in the ozone with her earmuff concert, but was quietly crying. When Crawford managed to raise an ear-piece and get her attention, he asked her two questions: was something wrong and did she know the whereabouts of her mother?

24

She jerked her head away, replaced the ear piece and answered cryptically, "No" and "No."

The President was accustomed to the mood swings of his daughter and gave no further thought to her reply.

A quick review with the staff yielded no usable information either, causing Crawford to think, "*Something is wrong.*" He summoned his Secret Service security chief and asked for a thorough check of the grounds and exit security to see if anyone had seen the First Lady.

By seven thirty p.m. no leads had materialized and a cursory search of the White House yielded no clues. The Security chief returned without any word and recommended alerting the D.C. police.

At just that moment Mal Willingham arrived and was ushered into the President's private quarters. Crawford had never seen the journalist so agitated. "What is it, Mal?"

"Have you found your wife?"

The President's negative answer produced a noticeable sag in Willingham's shoulders. His face seemed to age right in front of Crawford's eyes. "Mr. President, I believe your wife is dead by her own hand. This note was what she sent me today. Unfortunately, it was copied and sent to the news desk before I got it. I think I've squashed it, but can't be sure. I was hoping she would be here when I arrived."

Crawford took the note and began to read. His facial expression registered shock and disbelief. He sat hard and his hands began to shake. Suddenly he stopped, dropped the note and buried his head in his hands. He began to sob.

Willingham turned to the Secret Service Chief and said, "Quick, get the staff. We have to search the house thoroughly." *Surely not here*, he thought.

The night staff, security chief and Willingham quickly began a search of all the residence rooms of the house. The President gathered himself and joined the search.

The journalist found her. His heart sank as he opened the closet door. Shel was sprawled in the corner of the closet. Mal Willingham ran to the door and shouted down the corridor. The others came running at the shout, "I've found her."

When the children heard Willingham shout, they hurried into the Lincoln bedroom and crowded close to their father. Willingham was bent over their mother, gently patting her face and trying to get her to speak. Shel drifted in and out of consciousness, barely breathing. The Security chief pushed past Shelden to summon emergency medical help, but in his heart he was afraid that it was too late for anyone but the medical examiner.

Crawford sank to the floor sobbing repetitiously, "No, no, no." He held the First Lady's head on his lap cradling her like a child. Chip closed down. If there was any emotion inside his firm young body it did not show. There were no tears, no words. He just stood rigidly at attention with his fists clenched tightly at his sides.

According to Willingham's private notes that were never published, Shelden Crawford threw her Walkman against the wall and fell at her mother's feet sobbing, "Oh Mommy, Mommy, Mommy, what am I going to do now? Please don't go, please, oh please."

The emergency medical technicians arrived and took over. They worked feverishly over the First Lady. One of them operated a video head cam and all three of them took instructions from an on-duty surgeon at the trauma center at Bethesda Naval Hospital. Having found the empty pill bottles, they were instructed to start an IV and place her on O$_2$ immediately. By the time *Marine One*—the President's private helicopter—landed on the White House lawn, the paramedics found nearly normal vital signs, but the First Lady was unconscious and barely breathing. Shelby Denise Haverford Crawford was rushed to Bethesda Naval Hospital where trauma surgeons took over. They pumped her stomach and admitted her to the Intensive Care Unit. The staff of the White House and the hospital were sworn to silence. The press had to be controlled and some plans made for the children.

26

By midnight the First Lady's condition was listed as critical but stable. For no apparent medical reason, she was comatose, not having regained consciousness. Some combination of psychological stress and depressive drugs had sent her into a traumatic coma. She was on assisted breathing apparatus and under constant medical watch. It would be more than three months before there was a change.

Crawford and the children stayed until three a.m. The President's personal physician, Capt. Harold T. Watson, USN, had been called in and was waiting with the family. He persuaded them that there was nothing for them to gain by staying at the hospital. He encouraged them to go back home. He would stay the night and call them if there was any change.

It was three fifty-four a.m. when *Marine One* touched down again at the White House. Crawford could now more carefully read the notes his wife had scribbled. By the time he was through with the note addressed to him, sobs were coming in a way his children had never heard. As he got to the note addressed to their daughter, he staggered as though he had been struck in the back with an ax handle. The children jerked the papers from his near lifeless grip and began to read.

Crawford, sobbing, said, "Oh, children, what have we done. What have I done? This just can't be happening. Sheldie, is it true? Are you pregnant? How? Why? Oh, God, what are we going to do?"

For the balance of the night, no one addressed the issue of Shel's condition or Sheldie's pregnancy. That would come later. They sat on the floor and held each other.

Sheldie curled up in her dad's lap in a fetal position and cried with long body-wrenching sobs until her tears ran dry. That was, in itself, telling since she had not shown any emotion other than disdain for her parents for the past two years. Even Chip, slumped on the floor next to his dad, wept quietly.

Dawn found them in a state of suspended animation, broken only by a phone call from Deanna Gombac, long-time press secretary for the President. "Mr. President," she asked, "have you seen the papers? The tabloids are having a field day. And even the responsible press have sensational headlines."

Crawford gathered himself and replied, "No, I haven't seen the papers or watched the news. What do the press people think they know?"

He listened in stunned silence as Dee recounted the headlines that had already hit the street. The stories included excerpts from Shel's note. "Sir," she said, "I apologize for interrupting, but we have to strategize **now** and work on damage control."

The President said, "I'm sure you're right, but I can't do it right now. Get number two…no, belay that." (The *number two* euphemism was one he often used to identify the vice president, Kristie Whitman. Under pressure he frequently reverted to Navy SEAL vocabulary.) "Leave her out of this for the moment. I can't imagine what she could contribute. But get Mal Willingham over at the *Post*. Shel sent him the note. I want to know how this stuff got out. Then get the chief of staff and Mal in conference. The three of you can craft some options. Call me back in an hour."

"Your parents and in-laws have been trying to reach you," Dee said.

"I figured they would be," he said. "I'll talk to them later. Do whatever you need to do for Shelly's parents. Have a helicopter take them to the hospital."

"Do you want to talk to them now?" she asked.

"Not now," he replied. "I need to pull myself together."

Crawford suggested to the children that they all shower and dress. They were not keen on that idea, but finally acquiesced. Thirty minutes later the Crawfords reconvened in the study.

Sheldie broke the silence. "Daddy, I'm sorry about getting pregnant."

"Darling, an apology isn't going to take care of the problem," Crawford said. "If your mother is right, you're in your third trimester at least. And, you'll still be pregnant tomorrow. Today we have to focus on how to take care of your mother. I love you and we'll get through your problem, too."

Chip broke in, "What are we going to do, Dad?"

The President hesitated before answering. "Son, my guess is that we will have to live through some really hellish and mean-spirited reactions from lots of folks...from the press, the tabloids and the general public. We're going to be the center of a media circus for weeks, maybe months. Anything that can be exploited and exaggerated will be. You'll probably hear some unflattering things about me. Some will be true...some won't. For today, though, we have to get our act together and face the world in a press conference...then start making arrangements to get your mother the best care possible."

He paused, then continued, "Let's just focus on today. What we have to do right now is survive this day. There has to be a press conference, but maybe we won't have to be there. We have to contact my folks and your Mom's. I'm sure they've heard plenty already. I guess I ought to do that now before they hear any more of this. Do you want to be on the call with me?"

The children said nothing, but Sheldie picked up her dad's arm and crawled under it. Chip handed the phone to his father and stood behind him with his hands on his dad's shoulders.

The air was full of bittersweet, so pungent you could almost touch it. The only sound in the room was the touch-tone sounds of the telephone being dialed. They seemed inordinately loud in the silence of the room. Rocko took a deep breath, then responded to the ringing of the phone being interrupted by a voice at the other end of the line. "Dad, you heard?"

His father had heard, of course, and had been besieged by the media. He had been trying to call. His tone conveyed both sympathy and irritation.

"I'm sorry," Crawford said. "One of my staff people told me you were trying to reach me, but things have been so hectic I haven't been taking any outside calls. The press got the note before we did. We were at the hospital and were kind of cut off from the outside world. I just let my people handle everything."

"Your people didn't tell us a damn thing," his father said. "They acted as if I was a reporter for one of those tabloid newspapers."

"I'm sorry about that," Crawford said. "They're not prepared for something like this. I wasn't prepared for it." He could hear his mother in the background, phrasing questions for his father to ask.

"How's Shelly? That seems to be the only thing the media doesn't know."

"That's a question I can't answer, Dad. She's in a coma."

"How are the kids?" the senior Crawford asked.

"They're doing as well as can be expected," the President said. "I know I should have called you last night, but we were trying to take care of Shelly and put out brush fires at the same time. I need you and Mom right now. The kids need you. We don't have a lot of support here. If you could come, I could have a plane pick you up in Kansas City."

Crawford's father and mother agreed. The kids talked briefly to their grandparents before closing the connection. Then Crawford called Barry Roberts, the White House Chief of Staff. "Barry, I need a big favor. Can you get a jet to Kansas City by noon today and bring my folks here? I need them right now."

Roberts assured the President that his request would not be a problem. He said he would handle all the details.

This is the tough one, Crawford thought as he took a deep breath and dialed the summer home of Shelly's parents, Hamilton Harrison and Ellen Lacy Hampton Haverford, late of the ambassador's residence at the court of St. James in London. Haverford had spent much of his life working at Merrill Lynch, but had taken early retirement when called to foreign service by President George Bush. He retired from government service following the election in 2000 to pursue his hobbies of sailing and fishing from the family's summer home at Martha's Vineyard. They lived there from April to October every year. During the remainder of each year their address was usually a luxury cruise liner or exotic international hotel. They had just returned to Martha's Vineyard for the summer.

A decidedly British voice answered the telephone. "Haverford house."

"Leeds?"

"Yes, Mr. President," came the crisp reply. Crawford did not know the man's first name, but he had been the *major domo* of the Haverford household as long as he could remember.

"Have Ham and Ellen heard?" Crawford asked, referring to Shelly's parents by their first names.

"Yes, there was a special report on *Good Morning America* and one of your people called. Dr. Haverford has been trying to reach you. And the doctor is here with the madam."

"Put me through to him, Leeds."

"Dreadfully sorry, sir," the man said before transferring the connection.

When Shelly's father answered, Crawford said, "Ham, it's me, Rocko...and the kids. I don't know what to say. I'm so sorry. Nobody had any warning. I should have called you last night, but it was just too mind numbing. We didn't know that the note had gotten into the hands of the press until just a short time ago. Shelly is at Bethesda in a coma. It's still touch and go, but she's alive. Harold Watson is personally seeing to her. The kids and I are going back in a few minutes."

The words ran together in what seemed to be one breath. Ham Haverford was the one man in the world who completely intimidated Crawford. And the events of the day had done nothing to alter that.

There was a long silence at the other end of the line punctuated only by heavy breathing. "Then it's true," Haverford said. "We had hoped..."

"Yes, sir, I'm afraid...at least some of it. I think one of my staff contacted you. She was supposed to make arrangements to take you and Ellen to the hospital."

There was another cloying silence. "I'll have the Life Flight team from Brigham and Women's fly Shelly here," Haverford said. "Ellen and I will see to the rest. I have her new will. And, *Mr. President*, you needn't bother yourself about my daughter any longer." The words were bitten off with rancor and controlled rage.

"My God, Ham, Shelly isn't dead. She's..." He heard a click and was speaking to a dead line.

Crawford and his two children sat in silence. It was Shelden who finally spoke. "Daddy, Pop's just hurt. Mommy's his only child. He'll be all right."

Her words were a bit hollow against the enormity of the day.

The most powerful man in the world sat with his head in hands, thinking, *Dear God, I hope so, but right now I'm not sure of anything.* Before he could respond to his daughter, a knock on the study door announced the arrival of Dee Gombac, Mal Willingham and Barry Roberts.

Crawford stood, took a deep breath and said, "Kids, go call Mavis and get her to tend to your school schedules. You may just want to complete the balance of the year at home. And we'll arrange that if you like. It's only a month until school is out. If it's easier for you to stay home, let's do it. Come back here in thirty minutes and we'll see what we have to do next."

Turning to the trio who had arrived, the President asked, "OK, Mal, how did this get public?"

"Mr. President, the news isn't good. A copy boy picked up my mail last evening and saw the seal of the First Lady on the envelope. As best we can determine, he indulged himself a peek at the contents. He then made a photocopy before leaving the envelope in my in-box. We know a copy was made, because the first page of Shelly's note apparently jammed in the copier and the first copy was incomplete. He threw it in the trash. We can only assume that he corrected the jam and made a full copy. In light of what we are seeing and hearing, the young man has been busy selling his secret. By day's end, there will likely not be a news source, legitimate or sensational, that won't have a copy. He will be fired, of course, and we are exploring filing charges against him for theft by conversion, but it's like locking the barn after the horse is gone. I'm sorry."

"Mr. President," Dee said, "you must make a statement. The press corps is hammering me. So far I have been able to stall them with the *over-*

come by grief, we'll have a statement later in the day story. But that will hold them off only so long."

To the chagrin of the political pundits and the delight of the President, Roberts, the former executive officer on the Strike Force Alpha SEAL team with Crawford, frequently called his old and new boss *Commander* rather than *Mr. President.* He did so on this occasion. "Commander, we have to button up this situation publicly so we can get on with managing your family's problems. I propose that we craft a statement for Dee to deliver to the press corps that provides plausible deniability to the note and expresses your profound grief at the condition of your wife and partner for eighteen years and mother of your children. I suggest we use the grief angle until at least tomorrow at which time we may know more. Sooner or later, though, you will have to step forward with a statement. That will buy us a couple of days to make arrangements and get you all together. Sound good so far?"

For the first time since discovering Shel's comatose body, a glint of steel returned to the warrior President's eyes. It was the look that compelled Roberts and the fourteen other members of Naval Special Warfare Force Alpha to follow him into the hellholes of Kuwait and Lebanon. "Barry," he asked, "has anyone been working on a draft of the statement?"

"Mal and Dee have been working on an idea I think has merit," Roberts said. "Dee, read us what you have."

Dee said, "I think I should make the statement, with Mal, Barry and the vice president on the dais with me. Here's what we have so far. *Ladies and Gentlemen, I regret to inform you that some of the rumors flying about since early this morning are true. Dr. Shelby Denise Crawford was found unconscious at the White House last evening. She was rushed to Bethesda Naval Hospital where all state-of-the-art medical efforts to revive her were employed. Her condition is critical, but stable. The next ninety-six hours are crucial. Mrs. Crawford is in ICU at Bethesda and has not regained consciousness. The President and his children were with the White House staff when the First Lady was found unconscious.*

The President and his family have requested that they be given a few days to manage their own grief and make arrangements for the care of the First Lady. The President will come before you within the next couple of days with a statement. In the meantime, in lieu of flowers to the hospital, the First Family requests that donations be made to the Coalition for the Proliferation of Safe Nuclear Power Fund in honor of Dr. Crawford's long and extensive contributions to its work.

Much of what you have seen printed and heard broadcast has come from a note alleged to be from the First Lady. The source of the note is not known at this time, and until the original has been analyzed for authenticity, there will be no further comment on it at this time.

And then, we simply say *no questions* and walk away."

"Good, Dee, but make one change," the President said. "Make the donations to that scholarship fund that Haverford endows at Harvard. I called him this morning and he hung up on me. He's pretty angry with me at the moment and I need all the ammunition with him I can get.

"Anybody else have anything to add? Okay, when can we get a final draft and have you make the statement?

Willingham suggested they wait until after the noon hour to cut off the midday news broadcasts. They settled on two p.m.

"Okay, Barry, let's get to it," the President said. "Get Florence to come over here and set up in the study. She can handle pertinent calls for me from here. Then, can you come back and help me work out my scheduling rearrangements and what we are going to do about Shel's care? I want to spend some more time with my children and I'll meet you back here right after Dee makes the announcement."

The Florence to whom Crawford referred was Florence James. She had been the civilian liaison to Strike Force Alpha until he was elected President. He had persuaded her to leave the employ of the Navy and assume direction of his appointments staff."

The President sighed and continued, "Thank you all…you especially, Mal, for being here as my friend."

34

They stood to leave, but Willingham lingered for a private word. "Mr. President, I don't know whether to grieve with you, pity you or simply be angry. I'm your friend, but I'm sick to death of the way you have squandered privilege. I hope you're man enough to rise above this with honor and integrity and that you can salvage something of your family and your job. There are two, soon to be three, children in there and a wonderful lady lying in a coma who may never regain consciousness. They all need a man of integrity for a husband, father and grandfather. And, maybe more than you will ever know, the nation needs something positive from this fiasco. I hope you're man enough to make it happen. God help you if Shelly dies."

Ignoring the President's extended hand, he spun on his heel and left.

Willingham's combination admonition-lamentation caught Crawford by surprise. Before he could respond, the journalist was out the door. Sheldie came into the room, not in her usual uniform of baggy sweat clothes, but in a dress belonging to her mother that gave no small hint of the swelling hips and full breasts of a pregnant woman. "Daddy, can we talk, just you and me?"

The Prognosis

"Some medical conditions and healings occur for no apparent reason—at least no reason that can be explained by the practices of medicine. I do my best, and God does the rest."

HAROLD T. WATSON, M.D., CAPTAIN, USN

"Pop, how do you know all this stuff?" Ryan asked.

Grammy had just brought each of us a piece of hot apple pie for dessert. She then joined our three children and their families in the den where they were decorating for the Christmas celebration scheduled for the next evening. She was, as always, sensitive that Ryan and I were engaged in serious conversation and did not insist that we join them.

No matter how many times I see that gorgeous redhead, I am always as thrilled that she loves me as the first time she said so. As I have probably already mentioned, Barbara and I have been married for more than twenty-five years and it just keeps getting better. We were both married previously, so when we married, our children were college age. We decided to count our anniversaries by the month until we reached twenty-five. That would give us more anniversaries than our children had birthdays. This year we celebrated our "Golden Anniversary." Not bad!

Ryan and I retired to the verandah and the porch swing to finish our talk. I answered his question, "Well, some of these folks are now my good friends. And, we have had lots of time to talk about those days."

Ryan turned slightly toward me on the swing, probably remembering that the men in our family tend to get harder of hearing as they age. "Did President Crawford's in-laws ever get over being mad at him?"

I laughed and replied, "You are getting ahead of the story, pal. Let me get there. Indulge an old man. I told you I like to tell stories. Goodness knows I've told you enough in your lifetime."

•••

The President's family disagreed over the type of long-term care to provide for the First Lady. After the first critical ninety-six hours, her vital signs were stable. Brain activity seemed almost normal and improving, but she was still comatose and on assisted breathing apparatus. The President and Shel's parents were in agreement that they wanted no pomp and ceremony. Regardless of the location, low-key was the order of the day. Both families feared that any high profile public display would produce a carnival sideshow that would embarrass the family further. And, they did not give a damn about what was politically correct. Minimizing press access was paramount.

The Haverfords wanted to bring Shel to a private convalescent hospital near Boston. Crawford preferred the military security of Bethesda Naval Hospital.

In the end the President prevailed. Crawford's parents came to the White House and stayed with the children during the hectic days immediately after the announcement.

Ham Haverford anticipated the worst. To cool his anger toward the President, and to grieve privately, he took *Hamilton's Plumduff* out into the waters of the Atlantic near where his Shelly had grown up and prepared it for the funeral he was certain was to come. The *Plumduff* was the thirty-seven meter Perini Navi blue water sailing yacht Shel could not remember in her note. Ellen Haverford moved into a private VIP suite at Bethesda and was at Shel's side every day. Her husband would not come to the hospital if he knew the President was going to be there. Fred and Mary Crawford stayed until the first week in May when Fred had to return home to prepare for the wheat harvest.

It would take a long time for the relationship between Ham Haverford and Rocko Crawford to heal.

By May first, eight days after Shel had tried to take her own life, there was no change in her condition. The tabloids and the sensational TV magazines continued to have a field day, but the initial crisis was over. Now another crisis loomed with the dawning of the month of May.

Crawford tried to resume some semblance of his normal routine, but could get little done. Friend and foe alike still wanted to talk about Shel's note and condition. Governing by regular schedule became nearly impossible. No briefing or press conference could be held without incessant questions and speculations related to Shel's coma and Sheldie's pregnancy.

And, of course, there was still Sheldie to worry about.

The Crawford family decided to spend the summer at Camp David. The Vice President and cabinet would handle duties normally attended by the President. Crawford would lead from Camp David, away from prying eyes, and give himself some time to heal his family. He planned to keep *Marine One* at Camp David so he would be only minutes away from Bethesda in the event of any change in his wife's condition.

It was on May fourth that the family boarded *Marine One* and was spirited away for the summer. Every day in May one or more of them was at Shel's side. Crawford spent one day each weekend with his wife. It would be August before he again appeared before the nation as the most powerful man in the world.

Speculation, of course, ran rampant. Would he quit? Would Congress declare the Presidency vacant? Would the Vice President move to have the President declared incompetent to govern and assume the reins of government? The Democrats were having a political festival. There were few other topics on the nightly news or in the print media. It was setting up to be an interesting summer.

In the midst of it all, however, one amazing thing did occur. A large number of the power brokers inside the Beltway developed a sense of compassion that amazed even them. They closed ranks, regardless of their political affiliations, and worked together to protect this warrior chieftain and his children while they healed. Government continued to operate and Crawford was able to do the minimum things needed from him.

No one knew for sure when he would return to Washington for good—or if he would.

The Long Summer Angst

"A man who wants to lead the orchestra must turn his back on the crowd."

MAX LUCADO

Until nineteen fifty-three Camp David, Maryland, was known as *Shangri-La*. It had been a rural retreat for U.S. Presidents since its establishment in nineteen forty-two by Franklin Delano Roosevelt. Located in Frederick county in north-central Maryland, less than one hundred and twenty kilometers from Washington, the Camp site is inside Catoctin Mountain National Park, a unit of the National Park Service on a spur of the Blue Ridge Mountains. It is just west of Thurmont. The Campsite itself is situated on a scenic mountainous venue of two hundred acres, surrounded by maximum-security fencing and closed to the public. In nineteen fifty-three, President Dwight D. Eisenhower renamed it *Camp David*, after his grandson, and the name has remained the same.

Camp David, administered by the Office of the Military Assistant to the President, contains a presidential office and living quarters, swimming pool, meeting hall and several cottages—all named after trees such as the Aspen, Birch and Dogwood. The enclave was first made famous when FDR and British Prime Minister Winston Churchill met there during World War II. Since then there have been numerous high-level presidential conferences with foreign heads of state.

In September of nineteen seventy-eight, President Jimmy Carter intervened in the continuing crises in the Middle East. He brought Egyptian president Anwar el-Sadat and Israeli prime minister Menachem Begin to Camp David where they struck the monumental agreement known now simply as *the Camp David Accords*. These agreements continue to define relations between Arab and Jew until this day. The Camp David Accords led in nineteen seventy-nine to a negotiated peace between Egypt and Israel, the first of its kind between Israel and any of its Arab neighbors.

Camp David in the spring is an explosion of new growth. While no season at Camp David is without its special charm, spring and fall are particularly beautiful. Paths from the top of a small peak wind down past, and around, several of the cottages that are snuggled beneath and sheltered by a thick growth of stately oak, ash, poplar, locust, hickory and maple trees.

The proximity of the living quarters engenders an atmosphere of intimacy and isolation from outside influences that is conducive to easing tensions. There are golf carts and bicycles available, and over time there have been some apocryphal stories about harrowing escapes from disaster as these two means of transport have sought to coexist with foot traffic. One of those involved Amy Carter and members of the Camp David Accords guest list from the Middle East. Rumor has it that disaster was averted by the slimmest of margins.

For Crawford and his daughter, however, walking along the pastoral paths was to become the preferred style of locomotion.

•••

The White House staff expanded the full communications center at Camp David. In less than a day, the President had installed full motion broadcast quality video conferencing, additional secure encrypted phone and fax lines, all the secure hot lines and personal unlisted numbers via remote call forwarding for the children.

On arrival at Camp David, Crawford called his older sister, Rosemary. "Rosie, what are you doing?"

"Nice to hear from you, too, little brother," she said. The two of them had not been close. In high school he had been the handsome jock with the plain older sister. There had been little contact between them since the Gulf War. The sarcasm fairly dripped from her voice. "To what do I owe the honor of a call from The President himself?"

"Come on, Rosie," he said. "I'm in deep *caca* here. I know you and I haven't been close, but I need your help. I don't know anywhere else to turn. Please hear me out."

She still wasn't buying. "What do you want?" she asked.

No wonder she never married, he thought. *She's a tough old broad.*

Rosemary had graduated ahead of him at Olathe, Kansas, East High School in nineteen seventy-four and had gone on to Kansas State Teachers College at Emporia. She had excellent grades in college, but the stiff competition for medical school forced her to settle for the physician's assistant program at The University of Texas Medical Branch in Galveston. She never married.

For years she had worked small rural practices in South Texas. She was not only frugal, but had inherited a substantial sum from her maternal grandfather who died in nineteen fifty-nine leaving an estate valued beyond three million dollars. Coupled with her savings, she had sufficient income to retire after twenty years of practice. Her goal for the rest of her life was to research creative ways to bring the benefits of big city medicine to the back roads where she had dispensed health care for so long. She was particularly interested in creative low cost ways of bringing emergency medicine to rural residents where farm accidents created situations that local providers could not manage successfully. Many mangled limbs and lives that might otherwise have been salvaged were lost. If high quality trauma care could be made available within the first critical moments, many could be saved. She was busy researching, writing and soliciting grants from her home in McAllen, Texas.

"I don't know what to do with Sheldie," the President said, "and I don't want her subjected to outside medical care if we can avoid it. This is going to be tough enough as it is. Can you stay with us at Camp David for a few months? I'll get you some help on your research, anything, but please say you'll come. She has always liked you."

"You little prick," Rosie said, "that's not fair. If it were just for you, I'd tell you that it's about time you got what's coming to you. Sheldie is a different deal. I'll come. How do I get there?"

"I'll send you a ticket," he replied.

"I'll get my own ticket. You get me from Dulles to wherever you are."

He laughed. "Okay, just let me know when you're arriving and I'll have a car waiting for you. And, Rosie, thanks."

On the day Rosie was to arrive, Rocko decided it was time to sit down with Sheldie. Actually, taking a walk seemed like a better idea. He went to her room and knocked. "Honey, can we talk?" he asked.

There was no answer. He put his ear to the door and heard the faint sounds of the ever present Walkman. He knocked harder and heard her shuffle toward the door.

There was no life in her. "Hi, Daddy," she deadpanned.

"Let's go for a walk, Sheldie."

With no further words they linked arms and started off across the compound toward Aspen cottage, the Secret Service in tow. Crawford told Sheldie to wait a moment and went back to see the detail captain. On his return he explained, "I asked him to give us some more separation so we could talk in private."

I don't know what she's thinking, he thought as they again strolled in silence, *and I can't seem to find the right words to start.*

Sheldie rescued him. "Daddy, I'm so sorry," she began. "What happened to Mommy was my fault. I didn't mean to get pregnant. I thought I was doing all the right things to have safe sex. I even got the condom from school and everything." She was crying again. "Oh, Daddy, I'm so scared."

There was no belligerence, no disdain. She was his little girl again. "I've been on the Internet constantly since I knew for sure," she said. "I can't have an abortion this far along, but I pray every day that it will go away. What am I going to do?"

"Whoa, honey," Crawford said. "You're way ahead of me. I have a million questions like, *When did this happen? Who is the father? Where did you find the time and place to have sex? And, just how active sexually are you?* That's for openers. Fill me in if you don't mind."

She shuddered and began to cry a little harder. "Honest, Dad, this was only my second time. The first time was at camp when I was twelve. Remember when I went to the youth camp in the Catskills just before you were nominated for President. I really liked it…the sex I mean. But I was so scared that I didn't do it again until around Halloween last year."

The more she talked the smaller and more helpless she sounded. Crawford was no longer the President. He was a man and a father. He hugged his daughter tightly while she sobbed on. He stroked the luxurious mane of auburn hair that she inherited from him, and felt her warm body against his. Her tears soaked through the golf shirt under his open windbreaker. His eyes were wet, too.

Finally she pushed away and said, "The time and place were easy, Daddy. We sneaked into the bedroom just past the Lincoln bedroom at the other end of the house and locked the door. We did it right there on the bed. Then we sneaked back out and he went back to…"

"Back to where, sweetheart?" The harshness was evident in his voice.

"I don't want to tell you, Daddy. I'm afraid you'll hurt him. It's not his fault, Daddy. I egged him on…you know, like I was a prick-tease?"

"Where did you learn language like that, young lady?" he asked, angrily.

There was a sudden flash of the old Sheldie in her eyes and a hint of the sarcasm that had become her trademark over the past two years. "Oh please, Daddy, give me a break. I know a lot more than you think. How do you suppose I managed to get the health clinic to help me?"

"I was coming to that," he said.

"Kids do stuff like this all the time," she said. "I have a fake ID that says I'm nineteen. With this body I haven't had any problem making it pass."

He decided that finding where a President's daughter could get a fake ID was a question that could wait for another day. He would stick to one problem at a time. "Well, that explains the call your mother got from the clinic."

The mention of Shel shoved both of them back into their own thoughts and silenced their conversations for several more yards. Sheldie then moved closer to her father, put an arm inside his windbreaker and around his back. He mustered up the wherewithal to say, "Honey, it's important for us to talk about what we're going to do about the baby. Then we can talk about the father. What do you think your options are?"

She waited a bit to answer, then replied, "I know it's too late for an abortion, Dad, and even if it wasn't I'm not even sure I could live with that. Do you know Elizabeth Alden? She's in the ninth grade at school. She had an abortion last year and everybody knows. People walk around her like she has the plague. The only boys who want to have anything to do with her just want a piece of ass from her. I couldn't take that."

He was shocked again by the easy coarseness of her language, but resisted reprimanding her. At warp speed he was discovering that he did not know this child of his at all.

"I don't like the idea of having a baby either," she continued. "I'm not really as grown up as I look. And a baby...well, that's just too gross. I think about giving it up for adoption, of course. And I think about keeping it. But when I think about keeping it I realize that it might remind me that Mommy might be okay if this hadn't happened. I just don't know what to do."

She continued crying as they walked on. He knew he had to pick his words with the care of a bomb disposal squad choosing the right colored wire. "Darling," he said, "there are only two reasons you could consider an abortion this far into your pregnancy. If your health is at risk and maybe if you had been raped. Otherwise, we would have to break the law and send you off somewhere to have the baby taken. You are healthy as a horse and, by your own words, you weren't raped. Did the doctor examine you at the clinic and say anything about your health?"

She mustered a small laugh through the tears and said, "That's what the doctor called me...*healthy as a horse*...and no, it definitely wasn't rape. I invited him to do it."

The President looked at her, hurt in his eyes, and said, "Well, the next option is to start proceedings to have the baby adopted out at birth. Goodness knows there are lots of wonderful families who can't have children who would be glad to have the child. Have you given that any consideration?"

"Daddy," she said, "I've thought about it. I've wondered if the baby would have a good home if I did that. I've also wondered about what kind of person I am to even think about it. I've even wondered how the baby will feel when it grows up knowing I did that. There's a lot I've wondered about. I cry myself to sleep every night worrying whether this is my punishment for what Mommy did. I just can't get over that. Maybe having this baby and keeping it is part of my punishment."

He shook his head in resignation. "Sheldie, this has nothing to do with your mother. Your mother's problems were with me. I never treated her right. Not from the beginning."

"Then it's true that you screwed other women, Dad?"

Her words cut to the bone. Cut to the bone. Crawford had never wanted his children to know about the revolving women in his life. That his daughter even thought it caused him to feel small, evil and selfish. *Little girl of mine*, he thought, *how I wish I could rewind the clock. There's so much I would do differently.*

When Sheldie did not get an answer, she stuck out her chin and asked, "How come men who screw around are studs and women who do the same thing are sluts and whores? Why isn't it the same? What are people going to think about me?"

The President sat down on a rock outcropping. He put his head in his hands and began to cry. Sheldie sat beside him and attempted to apologize for her questioning, but he put his hand to her lips to shush her and hugged her close.

"Sheldie, I've been such a jerk," he said. "There's no other way to say it. I don't know what people are going to think about me either, so I'm scared, too. I've been to war in lots of places, but I've never been as scared as I am now. I can promise you one thing. I will never ever abandon you. I'm going to stick with you no matter what. I don't know much about being a dad. And, obviously, I haven't shown that I know anything at all about being a husband. But the one thing you can count on is that I'll be here with you. And, I'm going to learn."

More tears. He emptied pockets looking for more Kleenex. Finally they both took deep breaths and he said, "Honey, right now your options are either keep the baby or give it up for adoption. I'd like for you to talk to Aunt Rosie some more about this. She's coming to stay with us for a while so you can have regular medical attention without announcements in the press. I'm expecting her here today. She's a lot smarter than I am."

Sheldie brightened. She had always had a special bond with her Aunt Rosie.

"I have to ask you about the father," the President said. "Who is he?"

Her face clouded. "No, Daddy, don't make me tell you. I'm afraid you'll hurt him."

He sighed. "I'll admit that was my first thought, but not now. There's more than enough blame to go around for this. I'm at fault and so is your mother. She's at fault for not having the courage to confront both of us. You're at fault for not having enough commitment and knowledge to keep your pants on. The young man is at fault for not respecting you enough to tell you no."

He could scarcely believe he had said the words and was even more surprised that he meant them. "The young man in question has both the right and the duty to know and take responsibility for this baby's welfare," he said. "The sooner we get this out in the open the better for all of us. I promise I'll not be rude to him, scare him or hurt him…honest Injun, cross my heart, hope to be run over by a freight train." The latter phrase had been theirs when Sheldie was learning to talk. And, as always, it brought a smile.

He continued, "Does he know?"

She shook her head 'yes', which caused her father both relief and irritation. "What has he said?" Crawford asked.

She replied in almost a whisper, "He's really scared, Daddy." Then she sighed and continued, "I met him at the White House. And, he didn't recognize me as being your daughter. The day we met I was dressed up and had my fake ID with me. I told him I worked on the White House staff. He's Georgia Davenport's son, Eric. He's a sophomore at Georgetown and had come to the House to see his mother. She works for Florence, doesn't she?"

He nodded in the affirmative, noting that tears were again forming in her eyes. For some reason he found himself questioning how there could be any left.

"I told him that my Dad was real strict and that he could not call me," she said. "I told him I would have to call him. He gave me his phone number and we began talking every night. At first it was just boy-girl stuff. He would come by after school and a group of us would go get ice cream before we went home. We did all that right in front of the Secret Service guys. Eric thought they were bodyguards for some of the other kids.

"On the days I knew I was going to see him, I would dress up and ditch the sweats. He thought I was nineteen and that my name was Liza Sammons. Finally, one weekend when you and Mommy went away last fall to that conference thing in New York at the UN, I invited Eric to come to the White House and do it with me in the bedroom…you know, like where I said before. I really got him hot for the idea, Dad. Like…I mean…he was really steamed up about getting in my pants. I even stole a pair of Mom's bikini panties to wear.

"I told him to get a pass to come see his Mom and I would meet him at the South Portico. Nobody bothered me when I began talking to him so we just watched for our chance and slipped upstairs to our room. Then I gave him one of the condoms they give us at school and we just did it. And` it was wonderful that time, too. Some of the girls at school said it really hurt them the first few times, but it didn't hurt me. When

49

we were finished he kissed me and we sneaked back downstairs where he went to see his Mom, and I pretended to go back to work.

"We talked about it again every night and were making plans to get together again after Christmas," she said. "I had to make up stuff about why I couldn't see him before, and I told him that if my dad ever caught us he'd kill us both, so we had to be real careful.

"Then when I didn't have a period in December or January I began to worry. Finally, when I didn't have a period in February, I told Eric and told him that I needed to go find out. He told me to get a home test and if it was positive he would find out about how we could go to the public health clinic. It took us a month or so to work out the details.

"I got Sharon Ames, my friend from school, to help me. The day we had arranged to go to the clinic, Sharon went into the bathroom near the gym at school and hid in one of the stalls. I told the Secret Service detail that I was feeling sick and needed to go to the bathroom. Sharon was dressed like me and agreed to stay in the stall until we got back. She would call out and pretend to be me if anyone came to check but, fortunately, no one did. I changed into grown up clothes that Sharon had brought to the bathroom and put up my hair. Then I climbed out the window and Eric picked me up and drove me to the clinic. We were lucky, the doctor saw me quickly, and within forty-five minutes I was back in the bathroom at school. Sharon took my dress up clothes and I washed off all my makeup and let my hair down. I pretended to be sick at my stomach all the way home. And, if the Secret Service detail knew anything, they didn't let on. You know the rest."

Crawford was more than a little dumbfounded by his daughter's story. *At her age she already has the makings of a spy*, he thought. In fact, he knew people engaged in covert activities who were not close to being as imaginative. *How could we have left this precious vulnerable creature so unprepared for handling her little girl's life experience trapped in a grown woman's body?* His sense of failure was profound.

"Thanks for telling me," he said. "What has Eric's reaction been so far?"

She smiled and said, "He has been so sweet, Daddy. He offered to drop out of school and marry me when I told him. Then I had to tell him who I really was and that I was only fourteen. I thought he was going to croak.

"For days after I told him he wouldn't talk to me. When he finally answered his phone one night he told me he had been drunk for several days and was just sobering up. Knowing you're my dad, he was even more scared. He swore he wouldn't have come on to me if he had known I was only in the eighth grade. He's pre-law and he kept worrying about *statuary rape* or something.."

Her misuse of the word was not funny. "That's *statutory* rape, baby, not *statuary*," he said. "And it has to do with an adult having sex, even with consent, with an underage person. You qualify, but to his credit that's the right answer. I guess the important question is, do you think you love him?"

"I don't know," she replied. "We've had some fun and I get hot for him, but I don't know about love. How do you know? And besides, even if I do, I don't want to be married to him or anyone else right now. I've only been a teenager a year and a half."

He shook his head in resignation. "OK, Sheldie, I want to meet Eric Davenport. You call and tell him I'll send a car whenever he's available. You can also tell him that I won't kill him or hurt him. After all, he's the father of my first grandchild."

Again, she mustered a smile through her tears. "I'll call him, Daddy."

He sighed and said, "I do love you, Sheldie. And I always will. What has happened does not diminish that in the least. I'm disappointed, of course, but I'm sure you're disappointed in me, too. Let's make this the beginning of a new day between us. And, by the way, if Eric has told his mother, invite her to come too. If he hasn't, tell him to get busy and tell her. We need to get both of them to come out here. Is that all right with you?"

She was a bit hesitant about including Eric's mother, but in the end agreed that it was probably best. By this time they were back at the house. She went to her room and Crawford stood on the front porch contemplating what she had told him. The gray government car transporting Rosie that pulled into the circular drive interrupted his thoughts.

He greeted his sister, "I never thought I'd say so, Rosie, but damn...it's good to see you. I'm really lost here. Let's get you settled and I'll call Sheldie."

•••

The staff at Camp David included Barry Roberts; Florence James; Mavis Cortland, who did not have anything to do; the Navy lieutenant symbolically carrying the *football* (the briefcase containing all sorts of classified communications and military launch codes that accompanied the President wherever he traveled); the Secret Service detail and the domestic staff. Cabinet members, members of the JCOS, the National Security Advisor, the Senate Majority Leader and Whip, the Speaker of the House, and Dee Gombac came and went from time to time.

On May tenth, two thousand two Dee Gombac was at the Camp. She was there with leaders of both Houses of Congress to discuss the President's first address to the nation since the day the media dubbed *the tragedy at the White House.*

It had been almost three weeks since Shel had been rushed comatose to Bethesda Naval Hospital. The press and the nation were demanding a statement. A crisis in confidence was brewing and a response was mandatory.

"Barry, come join us," the President said. "I think we're ready for a trial run. All right, Dee, what do we have?"

"Mr. President, I think our best course is to continue to focus on your grief," she replied. "I think you should avoid any commentary on the First Lady's allegations of your misconduct. I also think it unwise for you to have any comment on Sheldie's condition. That's what this draft does. Want to give it a try?"

Crawford nodded, took the papers she offered him and began reading aloud. "My fellow Americans, there is no way to express either the sorrow or the profound sense of loss that my family and I are experiencing in the tragic condition of our wife and mother. I have two teenage children who need me very much these days as we put our personal lives back together. A significant part of our home has been whisked away unexpectedly and, perhaps, permanently. I would be remiss in my responsibilities as a parent if I did not take some priority time now to see to our healing. I could not be what I should be as leader of this great nation if my family is not my first priority now.

"Therefore I have moved our living quarters to Camp David...where we will stay through the summer months. During this time there will be uninterrupted communication links to the Oval Office. All functions of State requiring my attention will be met. I expect to minimize all travel and social events that are not deemed critical. Vice President Whitman and other senior members of this administration will either keep my schedule previously made for the summer months, or those activities will be rescheduled for the fall.

"On behalf of my family I thank you for your unprecedented outpouring of sympathy. For the cards, letters, e-mail messages and telegrams, we thank you. For the flowers sent to the First Lady...and for the donations to the Ham Haverford Endowed Chair in Finance at Harvard University in honor of my dear wife...we are profoundly grateful. Your caring thoughtfulness gives us the strength to carry on. Again, my profound thanks."

Turning to Roberts, Crawford asked, "What do you think?"

Roberts nodded appreciatively and replied, "I like it...but just a thought. Where you say *in honor of my dear wife* I am concerned that those who only have Shel's note will see that as insincere. I think it would be better said, *in honor of the First Lady.*"

They hammered away at the final language for another thirty minutes. The conference was set for ten a.m. May twelfth at the White House.

It would later strike Crawford as odd that no one had addressed the things Shel had accused him of in her note. Absolutely no time had been spent helping him craft answers to fend off pointed questions that were sure to come. He wondered how many of his staff besides Barry Roberts knew about his indiscretions and were too embarrassed to bring them up. Either way, he determined that if he survived he was going to insist on much more honest communication from his advisers.

•••

"Mr. President, Mort Dean, CNN. Is it true that your daughter is pregnant?"

Steely-eyed, Crawford replied, "Mort, I know you're a parent, too. So I hope you'll understand that I'm not going to drag my children through any more embarrassment than they have already suffered. I have no comment on your question."

"Mr. President, Sarah Wallace, *U.S. News and World Report.* The news reports of the First Lady's suicide note intimated numerous extra-marital relationships. What is your response to these allegations?"

"Sarah, I will not comment on that at this time."

Then the voices seemed to all come simultaneously, clamoring for reasons why Crawford was unwilling to respond. Amidst the din of voices were shouts of *cover up* and *scandal*. Mal Willingham rescued him by standing and shouting, "Thank you, Mr. President." It signaled the end of the press conference.

Crawford was overwhelmed by feelings of anger and bitterness toward the press corps. *They're like vultures hovering over road kill,* he thought. *They have no concern for our suffering. Their only desire is to sell news…and the more sensational the better. Good news doesn't sell advertising…and this fiasco is juicier than an international crisis, the Clinton/Lewinsky scandal or the O.J. Simpson trial back in the nineties.* Bill Clinton skated on the edge of technical truth and outright lie for most of nineteen ninety-eight about his sexual involvement with a twenty-one year old intern at the White House. The American people spent more than forty million dollars bringing that scandal to the public glare, *ad nauseum.* Simpson, a former star football player and second-rate actor, had been accused of killing his wife. Because of his celebrity status—and because of media coverage—his trial became a national obsession. And, because Simpson was black, his guilt or innocence became a racial issue. He had been found innocent by a jury, but was guilty in the minds of an overwhelming majority of Americans.

So now there's another celebrity on trial, Crawford thought, *and this time it's another President of the United States. And I can't play the race card. I can't even say I'm innocent.*

The post mortem of the press conference, or *event analysis* as the wordsmiths wanted to call it, was not pretty. The media, obviously, would give little attention to the priorities of state until the President's personal problems subsided—or until something juicier came on the scene to grab their attention. Until then the decision was to retreat to Camp David and continue with Plan A. There would be no more press conferences for a while.

•••

Rosie settled in and began teaching prenatal care to Sheldie. They became inseparable. In a way Rosie was more a mother to Sheldie than her own mother had been in recent years. In another way Sheldie became for Rosie the family she never had.

Rosie was able to transfer her certification to Maryland with very little fuss. This enabled her to prescribe the medications Sheldie needed. And, since Rosie had delivered hundreds of babies in rural South Texas, Sheldie was in good hands. Sheldie thought so, too. She and her aunt were nose-to-nose deep in conversation many hours each day.

With only a skeleton staff at Camp David, and the normal problems of conducting business via video teleconferencing over secure encrypted satellite links, the President's days were full. The media circus, of course, continued in full swing.

Chip and Crawford's father decided that a Kansas wheat harvest would be a good respite for both of them. The President agreed, so in mid May he hugged his son goodbye. Chip and his grandfather boarded *Marine One*, security detail in tow, and departed for a commercial flight to Kansas City. From there they would go to Olathe, Kansas, where Chip would spend the summer with his butt firmly planted in the driver's seat of a John Deere combine harvesting his grandfather's wheat crop. He would then spend some time in Nebraska, Wyoming and maybe Montana, before school started in the fall.

•••

It took longer than anticipated to get Eric and Georgia Davenport to Camp David. It was mid June before Barry Roberts and Florence James could convince Georgia Davenport that the President was not holding her accountable for Sheldie's pregnancy.

By then Sheldie was somewhere between seven and eight months pregnant and beginning to look it. Crawford noted that her face seemed brighter than usual—and recalled that the glow was like that which had been on Shel's face when she was pregnant with Chip and Sheldie. There was a combination of joy and sadness in remembering.

Sheldie had been adamant about meeting with her father and Rosie to coach him on what he was to say to Georgia and Eric Davenport on their arrival. She feared that her warrior father would do something drastic, or say something inappropriate. He assured them he would not play the role of horse's ass.

When the Davenports exited the government sedan that brought them to Camp David, Crawford could see the trepidation on their faces. Sheldie saw it, too, and gripped her father's arm tightly. Rosie patted him on the back from the other side.

"Georgia, welcome and thanks for coming," he said in greeting. "And you're Eric, of course." He extended his hand and the young man gripped and shook it, though somewhat timidly. "I'm Rockland Crawford," he continued, "but you already know that. Under the circumstances, though, it's kind of hard to know what to say. This is my sister Rosemary and, of course, you know Sheldie. Please come in."

It was awkward. Given his druthers, Crawford would have preferred a root canal in a dentist's chair without Novocaine.

Eric stammered out something about being sorry and his mother talked

56

about shame. The conversation between the parties was like a bad dream, the dialogue so stilted that it would have been rejected by the director of a *B*-grade movie. The consensus was that everyone wished it had not happened, but accepted the fact that it had. There was brave talk about making the best of it, which pushed the dialogue below the *B*-level. They explored the possibility of marriage and no marriage, of keeping the baby and of giving it up for adoption. The end result of the conversation was a decision to postpone making a decision.

Sheldie decided she did not want to hear from Eric for a while, though she had not heard much from him in the first place. Eric and his mother volunteered to help with Sheldie's expenses. The President attempted to object on the basis that Sheldie did not need the money, but Rosie quieted his objection by kicking one of his legs that was stretched out under the table. They agreed to reconvene later in the summer.

The five suffered through dinner together, then the Davenports left for Washington in the same sedan in which they had arrived. Crawford could not help but feel a special sadness for Georgia Davenport. She was a single mother, hard worker, and had to live with the fact that her only child would soon be an unwed father. The President had spent considerable time feeling sorry for himself for the shame that Sheldie and her mother were causing him, but he preferred his boots to those of Georgia Davenport.

His plan was to immerse himself in work and to dig deep inside himself to see where he had lost his way. All his life, everything he had ever touched had turned to gold, but suddenly it all seemed to be fool's gold. *Who am I?* he was forced to ask himself.

Who is Rockland Hamilton Crawford

"I don't know who my grandfather was.
I am more concerned to know what his grandson will be."

ABRAHAM LINCOLN

The facts were simple enough. Crawford was born July fifth, nineteen sixty, the second child and only son of Fred and Mary Crawford of Olathe, Kansas. He came into the world weighing nine pounds, five ounces and was twenty-one inches long. He was a healthy boy with a shock of dark hair and swarthy skin that spoke of his father's Osage Indian heritage.

Fred and Mary had grown up on large neighboring wheat farms near Olathe. They had ridden the school bus together until they were old enough to drive and then Fred had picked Mary up in his forty-seven Ford pick-up everyday until they graduated from high school in nineteen fifty-one. Mary went off to what was known then as Emporia State Teachers College and stayed two years. Fred went to work as a partner with his dad on the wheat farm. To the surprise of absolutely no one they were married Christmas Day, nineteen fifty-four.

Their first child, Rosemary, was born in nineteen fifty-six, two days before their second wedding anniversary.

Fred and his dad farmed eleven sections of their own and leased another four sections that were in wheat from early winter to the summer and in maize from the summer until it was time to plant wheat again. Mary's father and three older brothers owned twenty-seven sections of prime wheat land and were the leading wheat producers in the county.

Rocko Crawford had grown up working the wheat plantings and harvests—and playing football for the Olathe East High School Hawks. In nineteen seventy-seven he was named to the second team all-state football squad as a running back.

Crawford wrote an essay while in high school that got the attention of Senator Bob Dole, native son of Russell, Kansas. The Senator was so impressed with the young man that he recommended Crawford for appointment to the U.S. Naval Academy.

Crawford entered the Naval Academy in the fall of nineteen seventy-eight and quickly distinguished himself academically, especially in military science. Faculty members labeled him a consummate warrior before the end of his first year. He was also a running back on the football team.

If there was any aberration in his character it was his conquest of women. He liked them all—and developed quite a reputation of being able to secure the attentions of any woman he wanted. He proved his reputation over and over with frightening regularity.

In his third term he met Shelby Denise Haverford, who was teaching quantum physics and tactical nuclear weapons. Haverford, a Ph.D. from MIT, was a civilian professor assigned to teach her specialties at the Academy during the sabbatical of a senior professor who had held the chair in *tactical nukes* for more than fifteen years.

After the first day of class several of Crawford's classmates determined that Dr. Haverford was the quintessential challenge to his unbroken string of conquests. She had enough impediments to make faint even the stouthearted.

Shelby Denise Haverford was the only child of Hamilton Harrison Haverford and Ellen Lacy Hampton Haverford. The Haverfords were born to the highest of society in Boston. Both came from old money. *Ham* Haverford, however, did not rest on the laurels of his family fortune. He distinguished himself first as a Harvard graduate and later as a professor at his alma mater. While a professor of financial strategy he gained an international following through his impromptu consulting practice with major financial institutions in both Boston and New York. He was recruited before age forty to head the leading edge products division of Merrill Lynch, where he recreated his family inheritance and more over the next ten years.

President George Bush tapped Haverford for the ambassadorship to the Court of St. James in London, where he served until his ultimate retirement after the election of two thousand.

Ellen Lacy Haverford was a tall, dignified lady who continued to turn heads when she entered a room. At five feet, nine inches and one hundred and twenty pounds, she had a figure that she had passed on to her daughter and granddaughter. Had she been disposed to do so, she could have been a beauty queen finalist as a young woman. In a word, she was sculpted beauty of indeterminate age. She would always look substantially younger than her age. She prided herself in remaining trim and fit. Her blonde hair never required more than highlights to retain its original color, and coupled with her large green eyes, always drew attention wherever she went. She distinguished herself not by her educational or financial acumen, although she was an honors graduate of Smith College, but by her innate ability to host the most elaborate functions with flair and aplomb. Affairs of the financial world and of State suited her to a tee. Few social events in Boston failed to compete to have her on their steering committees.

Shelby had grown up in the lap of privilege, but took after her father in the pursuit of excellence not inherited. She was an accomplished sailor and enjoyed life most when the family summered in Martha's Vineyard. She had developed quickly physically, so that by the age of fourteen she was elected queen of every school event that came along. In summers her deep tan, shining blonde hair and large brown eyes always drew a crowd of admiring eyes. In fact, the skimpy bikini swimsuits she wore made her look as if she had stepped off the pages of the annual *Sports Illustrated* swimsuit edition.

Shelby was a distinguished scholar—National Honor Society in prep school, Magna Cum Laude and Phi Beta Kappa graduate of Wellesley College. She had M.S. and Ph.D. degrees from MIT in quantum physics and had developed a particular interest in the application of nuclear power in tactical weapons systems. Her dissertation examining the possibilities of creating *clean* tactical nuclear devices was considered by scholars to be a classic. It was her work at MIT that landed her the visiting professor role at the Academy where she first met Midshipman Rockland Crawford. The year was nineteen eighty-two.

The bet classmates made with *Studs* Crawford was that he would be unable to work his magic on Dr. Haverford—and bring evidence of such magic in the form of a pair of the lady's panties. His classmates were counting on the impediments of the five to six year difference in their ages, Boston society versus a Kansas wheat farm and professor versus student. They figured these would be barriers that even the *king-of-the-broads* could not overcome. Crawford did not even blink covering their bets.

Shelby had just ended a three-year relationship with one of her father's Merrill Lynch protégés. The appointment to the Academy softened the blow of rejection that had come when the man she thought she would marry suddenly eloped with an air-headed blonde who was only nineteen. The truth was that the guy was not able to cope with Shelby's intellect.

Shelby was quite aware that she looked better than good, but that her IQ frightened off many men. She often looked at her naked body in the full-length mirror of her VIP quarters at the Academy—and she admired what she saw. She was also aware that every midshipman at the Academy looked at her with both admiration and lust. Though it was fall, tiny tan lines were still evident from her summer of sailing. Even with the admiring stares—and knowing that very few women looked better at age twenty-six—loneliness and hurt did strange things to her heart.

Early in the semester Shelby noted that Crawford was excelling in the above-the-norm atmosphere of her class. He even requested extra work. And if others did well to write a ten-page brief, he had no difficulty writing fifteen.

Initially there was time spent in academic pursuits, then an occasional *accidental* meeting over lunch, chance encounters at restaurants and, finally, bolder declarations of interest—an invitation to the festivities surrounding the Army-Navy football game.

The initial shock of Crawford's interest gave way to some latent recognition that she was, indeed, drawn to this handsome farm boy from Kansas. *Nonsense,* she had thought. *I'm at least five or six years older. When he graduates as an ensign in the regular Navy I'll be back at MIT. This is just a reaction to the rejection last summer.*

Still he persisted and, to her surprise, she agreed to meet him for a drink at one of the anticipated celebrations after the Navy goat once again kicked the Army mule's ass. So she went, almost backing out at the last minute. *But hey, what's the worst that can happen?* she thought.

She met him at the bar in the Adams Mark Hotel where the celebration was in full swing. In less than five minutes, noticing the eyebrows that were raised, she knew it was probably a mistake. She felt fortunate that none of her faculty colleagues saw her with the young midshipman—even though he was the best looking midshipman in the room.

Prior to the Christmas break Crawford learned that Shelby was meeting her parents in New York to spend Christmas at a residence they owned in the Hamptons. A short time later he engaged her in casual conversation and asked about her Christmas plans. When she told him he said, "No kidding? I'm going to New York for Christmas, too. Where do your folks live in the Hamptons?"

He knew, of course, but when she told him he shook his head in mock dismay and said, "No kidding? My friends live just down the way from there about a mile." It was a lie. She would later learn that he had researched the area and had found a house for sale near the one owned by her parents. He told her his friends were moving to Florida and had asked him to stay in their house during the holidays to dissuade would-be burglars. He told her he was glad to take them up on the idea because he had always wanted to spend Christmas in New York—to go to Macy's, Bloomingdales, FAO Schwartz and the Radio City Music Hall Christmas show. The truth was that he had reservations at the Hilton Hotel at John F. Kennedy Airport.

It was an elaborate scheme that depended on a number of things falling into place. And they did. "Say, Dr. Haverford," he said, "I have two tickets to the Radio City Music Hall Christmas Show for December twenty-first and don't know a soul in New York. Any chance you might like the other ticket?"

He had rolled the dice and come up with a seven. It was a free evening for her and she did want to see the Christmas show. He offered to drive them to the city, but she said, "No, Daddy's driver can take us and we won't have to worry about parking." He agreed to her offer, then frantically called looking for two available seats for Radio City show. He ended up paying a scalper double for them.

Crawford flew into JFK on December nineteenth and settled into the hotel. He then drove his rental car to the Hamptons. It took longer than he anticipated. He cruised around until he found the house where his alleged friends lived and then drove past the Haverford estate. Saying he had friends in the Hamptons had been risky, given that the Haverfords might have known who owned the house, but he figured the stakes were worth the risk.

His scouting mission complete, he returned to his hotel room to relax for a day and get ready for the big challenge.

He arrived early for their *date* on December twenty-first and was ushered into the house by Leeds, the butler and chief of staff of the Haverford homes. He had debated about what to wear. He settled on a new dark blue Brioni suit with a white-on-white shirt with monogrammed French cuffs, a red tie and the spit shined shoes he wore with his dress uniform. His mother had sent him a cashmere overcoat as a Christmas present that year. His folks, of course, were disappointed that he would not be in Kansas for Christmas.

Ham Haverford came into the library where Leeds had deposited him and, with a strange mixture of Boston and British English acquired over the years, said, "So you're the brash young student who is polishing up the professor."

"No sir," Crawford said, "I'm just a Christmas tourist who, by a quirk of fate, is just up the street from my favorite professor and alone for Christmas. Your daughter has graciously agreed to keep a poor Kansas wheat farmer from getting in trouble in the big city. I'm Rockland Crawford, sir."

Before Haverford could respond Shelby floated into the room, which caused Crawford's heart to skip a beat. She was wearing a black dress that looked as if it had been applied from a can of spray paint. A string of pearls the size of the marbles he had played with as a kid was draped around her neck. Dark hose, heels and a mink coat draped over her arm made up her ensemble.

"Hi, Daddy," she said. "I see you've already met Mr. Crawford. How do I look?"

Haverford grunted and managed a daddy-like smile. Crawford could think of nothing to say that would not telegraph how horny her outfit made him feel. Finally he took a deep breath and managed to say, "Marvelous."

She laughed a distinctively easy laugh to which he had become accustomed—one that he found himself thinking about all too often. *I wonder if this is getting to be more than just a damn bet*, he thought.

"Want a drink before you go?" Haverford asked.

"I don't think we should, Daddy. It's a bit icy out there and we don't want to be late. Perhaps when we come back. Is that all right with you, Mr. Crawford?"

"Yes, ma'am," he replied.

She laughed and said, "Look, this student-teacher language is a bit awkward under the circumstances. I'm Shelby...Shel to my friends.

And, of course, I know your first name is Rockland. But is that what your friends call you?"

"Well ma'am, my friends call me Rocko…or just Rock."

She laughed again. "Well, that settles it, Rocko. Let's be off to Radio City and see if the Rockettes have forgotten how to kick since last year."

He took her coat and placed it over her shoulders. The distinctive scent of an Estee Lauder fragrance filled his nostrils. She brushed up against him getting into the coat, took his arm, gave her father a peck on the cheek and they were off.

A man who appeared to consider words too valuable to be wasted drove them to the theater in a stretch limousine. The show, Crawford thought, was magnificent. Shel seemed to share the sentiment. During the performance she continued to hold his arm and press the firm flesh of a breast up against one of his triceps. Lucky tricep.

They small-talked their way through the program, which for him was over all too soon. When they exited the hall the long black Lincoln was right out front. The driver asked, "Dinner?" Without responding to him Crawford said to Shel in his best Rhett Butler imitation, "Miss Shelby, I have taken the liberty of reserving us a table by the dance floor at the Rainbow Room. I'm told the food and atmosphere there are more than acceptable for a lady such as yourself…and that the music is passable fine as well. May I have the honor of your company for dinner?"

She laughed, tilted her head to the left with a quizzical look and replied, "Why Mr. Butler, I'd be proud."

Crawford was grateful for the stoic Haverford chauffeur. He did not have a clue as to the location of the Rainbow Room.

The *art deco* decor and prestigious service made Crawford feel as if he had been transported to another time. "Crawford…party of two. Check your coat? This way, please. Watch your step." He realized such places were not new to his date, but they were new to him. The food was elegant. The prime rib he ordered could be cut with a fork—and the grilled salmon

Shel had almost made him want to order again. For a wheat farmer midshipman it was a far piece from home.

Later, after dinner drinks and coffees, they tried the dance floor and he thought she danced even better than she looked and smelled. *And, that's hard to believe*, he thought.

On the way back to her parents' home he whispered, "Shel…Dr. Haverford…I have a confession to make. When I first met you I thought you were the prettiest woman I had ever seen. I wanted to see if it were possible for a Midshipman to get a date with the distinguished lady Ph.D. on loan from MIT. I've done everything I could to attract your attention in hopes of a night like this. I even bet some classmates that I could do it. Attracting women has never been difficult for me. And, I don't mean to brag, it's just so.

"I'm confessing that to you now because I think I am falling in love with you. You're so easy to be around. I feel comfortable when I'm in your company. I don't want this to end. And, I sure don't want to screw it up. I know you're older than I am, but not by much. Is there a chance that you and I might see each other again?"

He knew his little speech sounded stilted, but he could not help it. This night with this woman was like no other in his twenty-one years. His confidence with her was not as it was with other women. He was afraid she would laugh and tell him to go away.

She smiled, turned on the seat until her knees were touching his thigh and took his hand in hers. Her big brown eyes stared intently at him as she again tilted her head. The silence was momentary, but for him it seemed like there was time enough to walk to the moon and back. "Rocko Crawford," she said, "I can't believe I am doing this. But, despite all the reasons I shouldn't be, I'm very attracted to you, too. I thought you were just a sweet boy here alone for Christmas until I drove by the place you said you were staying and discovered that we own that house. Daddy took it in a trade on a stock transaction and nobody lives there.

"I knew then how much effort you had put in to coming here to spend time with me. I thought the least I could do was give you a taste of society life in New York before we resumed our roles as teacher and student. I won't play games with you on campus. That's business. But here... this holiday...and any other time we can get away until it isn't fun anymore...I'm game to see where this leads us.

"In another year you'll graduate from the Academy. By then it may be over. If not, well...Fair enough?"

He could not speak. He just nodded and broke out into a smile that was so big it nearly swallowed both ears. And, it was not like him to be speechless.

"Now kiss me, sailor," she said, "and that's an order."

"Aye, Aye sir, ma'am!"

And so it began. Before the holiday was over, he told her about the panties he had promised and she took off the pair she was wearing and gave them to him on the spot.

They spent as much time together as possible until the term was over. Then she went back to MIT for the summer. But they wrote to each other often, spent holidays together and she was there for his graduation.

The passion remained alive and well. He thought it would never go away.

•••

Crawford put in a Special Request Chit at the Academy during his last semester for acceptance in the SEAL program. He scored the second highest ASVAB score (qualifying exam) ever recorded in the history of the SEAL program since its inception in nineteen sixty-two by President John F. Kennedy. He was at the optimum age of twenty-three at the time of his application and everything else was just perfect—EAOS, diving physical, pressure and oxygen tolerance test were all above the norms.

His Personal Action Request (form 1306/7) arrived at Specwar/Diver Assignment, NMPC 401D, Department of the Navy, Washington, DC, Phone COM 703-614-1091 (AV) 224-1091/92, along with his ASVAB scores, physical screening tests, diving physical record (form SF88-

SF93), pressure and oxygen tolerance results and his most recent performance evaluation report.

There were also letters of commendation from the vice admiral who served as commandant of the Academy and from Senator Bob Dole.

Upon acceptance he was transferred to San Diego, California, to begin Basic Underwater Demolition/SEAL (BUD/S) training. Most of the trainees were enlisted men. Officers assigned to the training program wondered why Crawford wanted such an assignment. His response was that he had always been the best at whatever he did and that the SEALS were the best the Navy had to offer.

The first phase of the training was nine weeks of basic conditioning. Crawford easily passed the fifty meter underwater swim, drown proofing and basic life saving tests. The one-half and three-quarter mile pool swims without fins were a snap. He beat all the other trainees by a wide margin in the one-mile pool and bay swims.

The two-mile ocean swim with fins was finished in a course record of forty-one minutes and six seconds. He ran the four-mile time trial in twenty-one minutes and forty-three seconds and topped off basic training with records in the fourteen-mile run and obstacle course. It would be twelve years before his marks were surpassed.

The second phase of training was seven weeks in length and concentrated on combat SCUBA diving. Crawford was introduced to two types of SCUBA gear: open circuit (compressed air) and closed circuit (100 percent O_2). The goal was to prepare the SEAL trainees as basic combat divers able to transport themselves from a launch point to a combat objective. This was *the* skill that separated SEALS from all other Special Operations Services.

The third phase of SEAL training was a nine-week course in demolitions, reconnaissance and land war. The trainees were taught land navigation, small-unit weapons and tactics, patrolling techniques, rappelling, infantry tactics and military explosives. The final five weeks were spent on San Clemente Island applying what had been learned in a practical environment. Simply put—war games.

Upon graduation from BUD/S, Crawford was assigned to Ft. Benning, Georgia for an intensive three-week basic parachute training program at the Army Airborne School. There were lots of stories about the combative competition between the guys in the funny little green hats and the eight SEALS who trained together. Ft. Benning was where Crawford got the triangular scar over his left eye. It was reported widely that Crawford walked away from the fracas, but the green beanie had to be carried away.

Following two more weeks of Special Operations Technician Training at the Naval Special Warfare Center on Coronado Island there was a six-month probationary assignment. Crawford was lucky enough to be transferred to Pensacola, Florida, where he learned the basics of flying both fixed wing and rotary aircraft. He would never be a combat pilot but in a pinch could fly out of nearly anywhere in virtually anything designed to fly. This training was over and above the continuing SEAL training that he did every day.

The sixteen-man platoon to which Crawford was assigned continued to run, swim and practice every day. Proficiencies were honed in free-fall parachuting into the ocean from ten thousand feet. More than once the team traveled in a RHI (rigid hull inflatable) boat one hundred miles across open sea to conduct a mission and then back to sea for twenty-five to thirty miles to rendezvous with a submarine. Their training theme was that 'the more you sweat in peacetime the less you will bleed in war.'

Commander William "Bull" Jimison, USN, took Crawford under his wing at Pensacola and was largely responsible for getting him promoted to Lieutenant junior grade.

By the time he had finished the course Crawford could fly fixed and rotary wing aircraft, combat SCUBA dive, HALO (high altitude low opening) parachute jump on land and water, many forms of hand to hand combat, proficiency in a variety of small arms and explosives, underwater demolition training, counterinsurgency, search and rescue and several forms of breaking and entering that would get a person arrested in civilian life.

70

From the summer of nineteen eighty-three until the summer of nineteen eighty-four, he was assigned as junior officer to a SEAL team that was active in a number of theaters around the world. These missions were classified. His skills were honed razor sharp under fire more than once during that year.

Shel and Crawford rarely saw each other during this period. Shel had a new assignment at MIT while he was away on a project for Naval Ordinance completing an M.A. degree at Georgetown University.

In June of nineteen eighty-four Crawford was offered his choice of permanent assignments. A SEAL team of sixteen men was being formed at the Naval Station, Norfolk, Virginia. He chose that one, was named the exec of the team and was promoted to the rank of lieutenant, USN.

To celebrate his permanent duty status, Crawford suggested, and Shel agreed, to become his bride. They were married in Martha's Vineyard at the end of the season, September twenty-ninth, nineteen eighty-four.

Shel continued to do research for the Navy and Crawford polished his skills as a Navy SEAL. They lived in Virginia Beach, Virginia, right on the Chesapeake Bay. He commuted to the Naval Station at Norfolk and Shel commuted to the Academy where she had acquired a permanent research position.

The *Chip* off the old Rock was born December twenty-sixth, nineteen eighty-five. They named him Rockland Hamilton Crawford, Jr. after Crawford and his grandfather, Ham. They decided to call him "Chip" sometime during his first year and the nickname stuck.

It was also during the first year of Chip's life that Crawford first slipped his wedding ring off and found comfort in the arms of another woman. He could not remember her name or face, but he did remember the event. Shel was busy with the baby and he felt left out and alone. It was not the last time he cheated on Shel. It got easier every time.

Crawford's duty assignments kept them in Virginia Beach. On January eleventh, nineteen eighty-eight the couple had their second baby. They named her Shelden after her mother. They combined Shelby and Denise and called her Shelden, or usually Sheldie. She was beautiful, even as a baby.

With Crawford's income and Shel's trusts, she really didn't have to work anymore and with Sheldie's arrival she decided to stay home and be a full-time mom for awhile.

Meanwhile, Crawford was quietly building a reputation as the toughest Navy SEAL team leader in the service. His became the elite team and was called upon for covert assignments that proved it. Much of what they did is still classified. Nevertheless, when he was promoted to lieutenant commander before age thirty, it raised some eyebrows in the Navy. He was one bad dude. When the services of Naval Special Warfare Force Protection were sought out, his team got first call.

Crawford was not home often and could hardly be classified as much of a husband or a father. Shel, on the other hand, was a good mother.

By the time the Gulf War ended in nineteen ninety-one, Shel had put Sheldie in nursery school and Chip was in first grade. She decided to resume her interest in nuclear physics. She received a grant to study alternatives for containment of nuclear escapes/meltdowns at nuclear-fired power plants from the Coalition for the Proliferation of Safe Nuclear Power.

It was the cause to which she devoted her public service life until two thousand two. Even when her interest in everything else waned the Coalition was her one surviving passion.

It was during this period that Shel began to drink...at home...alone. Much of her research work was done on the Internet/Intranet access , and so, she was alone much of the time. Drinking became a crutch for her loneliness and denial.

In nineteen ninety-one, nineteen ninety-two, and two thousand, three key events became the defining moments of Crawford's life.

First Defining Moment

"The best prize life offers is the chance to work hard at work worth doing."

THEODORE ROOSEVELT

From September second, nineteen eighty until August of nineteen eighty-eight, Iraq and Iran were at war. Iraq invaded Iran and for years the fur flew. Hundreds of thousands of casualties occurred.

The United States first became involved on May seventh, nineteen ninety when Iraq attacked the *USS Stark* in the Persian Gulf killing thirty-seven American sailors. It marked the first time Commander Crawford's SEAL team was deployed in the Gulf. The first defining moment in Rocko Crawford's life began on July seventeenth, nineteen ninety when Saddam Hussein accused Kuwait of overproduction of oil and theft of oil from the Rumaila oilfield, which Hussein claimed belonged to Iraq.

On August second, nineteen ninety Hussein invaded Kuwait. President George Bush froze Iraqi and Kuwaiti assets in the United States and the United Nations called upon Iraq to withdraw immediately and unconditionally from Kuwaiti soil. Hussein's response was to take his very sophisticated modern army and annex Kuwait on the strength of some ancient map lines that indicated Iraq's previous ownership of the Rumaila oil fields.

Kuwait's fall was swift and complete on August eighth, nineteen ninety. Saddam Hussein declared Kuwait annexed by Iraq. Over the next six months or so the events known as the Gulf War, or *Desert Shield* and *Desert Storm* played out.

In August of nineteen ninety the U.S. began interdicting Iraqi shipping and President Bush called up America's military reserves to active duty. The Iraqi army stormed numerous diplomatic missions in Kuwait City, including the U.S. Consulate, but all consular officials were safely evacuated. Political bickering in the U.S. and international posturing characterized the remainder of the year.

In January of nineteen ninety-one the mood of the country changed and Congress voted to allow U.S. troops to be used in offensive operations. A deadline was established for implementation of United Nations Resolution 678 for Iraq to withdraw from Kuwait or face reprisals. By January sixteenth, *Operation Desert Shield* became *Operation Desert Storm* as U.S. warplanes launched attacks on Baghdad, Kuwait and other military targets in Iraq.

One of the more frightening days of the war was January seventeenth, nineteen ninety-one when Iraq launched the first SCUD missile on Israeli territory, which precipitated deployment of U.S. Patriot anti-missile missile batteries in Israel. By January thirtieth more than five hundred thousand U.S. and U.N. troops were poised to attack Iraq. Over the next three weeks, war preparations continued. On February twenty-second President Bush issued the ultimatum of February twenty-third for Iraq to withdraw from Kuwait or suffer the consequences. Bush gave Saddam until noon Saturday to leave Kuwait. The pullout had to begin by noon, be completed in one week and within forty-eight hours Iraq had to be out of Kuwait City allowing the Kuwaiti government to return.

Saddam ignored the ultimatum, so early Sunday morning the allies launched a blitzkrieg-like ground attack. Within a hundred hours the war was over.

The first defining moment of Rocko Crawford's life was the period between February twenty-first through twenty-fourth of nineteen ninety-one. The Tom Clancy best seller *Nuclear Fire and Brimstone* that was made into a movie with Harrison Ford playing the U.S. Navy SEAL commander is loosely based on the events of these same days.

U.S. intelligence reports indicated that part of the scorched earth policy of Saddam Hussein was to deploy a very dirty nuclear device, crude but lethal, that his scientists had secretly prepared and spirited away from the Iraqi nuclear plants before they could be destroyed by U.S. war planes. The source of the fissionable materials and their actual make up is still classified.

However, less than one year before the Gulf War, two lead containers were dredged out of the Tigris River in northern Iraq with markings identifying them as part of more than one ton of weapons-grade plutonium stolen from the Chelyabinsk 67 Complex in southwestern Russia. Site investigation uncovered more than thirty metric tons of plutonium in an old converted warehouse with a small padlock on a wooden door as its only security. It was an unguarded site without even a telephone on the premises. Assuming that this material was converted into a crude nuclear device, it would have been one of the largest nuclear devices ever exploded, more than twenty times greater than anything ever tested.

Under a cloak of the smoke and soot from the hundreds of oil well fires lit by the Iraqis to deter air attacks over Kuwait, an elite team of the Republican Guard had secured the nuclear device within the confines of the largest oil tank farm staging facility in Kuwait. It was set to detonate within a specified time period unless the U.S. agreed to withdraw its troops and cease hostilities before sunup, February twenty-fourth.

Fallout estimates from the multi-megaton device were estimated to be lethal to more than two million people living east of Kuwait in Iran, Pakistan, Afghanistan, Bangladesh, southern Russia and as far east as India and Vietnam. It would have created a nuclear desert in Kuwait for two hundred years or more. It would have created illness, skin disorders, blindness, birth defects and other human casualties among more than forty million additional people over a vast area stretching across southern Asia, and perhaps airborne, to the west coast of the United States.

At a hastily called meeting of the President's war council on February nineteenth, the decision was made to deploy an elite SEAL strike team to locate the device and disarm it prior to the Sunday deadline. The proximity of Rocko Crawford's team at Norfolk and his reputation earned them the assignment.

Hurriedly briefed, the eight-man team departed via military jet transport for the Middle East. They rendezvoused with the *SSN/724 Louisville* (the nuclear submarine out of San Diego, California, used to launch Cruise missiles on Iraq) and proceeded to within fifteen miles of the coast of Kuwait. The team launched their RHI from the submarine and with a silent motor running at ten knots made their way to within one "click" (military idiom for *kilometer*) of the beach by two a.m. Gulf time February twenty-second.

Equipped with open circuit SCUBA gear, the team came ashore on the beach at the exact point of insertion outlined earlier aboard the sub. They were guided by an experimental hand-held GPS (global positioning system) locator that today is common for hunters and hikers to carry, but then was relatively new. It provided specific longitude and latitude positioning from a geo-synchronous satellite orbiting over the target area to within a fifty-meter accuracy.

The SEAL Team stripped their black wet suits and buried their SCUBA gear on the beach . Their assault uniforms and face paint were desert camo.

Each team member was equipped with a Heckler & Koch Mark 23 .45 caliber automatic handgun fitted with a three inch suppressor and modified to shoot single-shot double-action or in three round bursts with a selector and an infrared laser targeting system. Each man had ten spare clips affixed to a combat belt.

Five team members also carried H&K MP5 compact submachine guns featuring 9mm parabellum rounds. These weapons were also suppressed, infrared targeting equipped and capable of single shot, three round bursts or full automatic fire at eight hundred rounds per minute. Each man carried twenty spare clips in various pockets in their desert camo uniforms.

Two team members carried M-16 A3/M4s with M203 40mm grenade launchers. Each of the eight-team members carried four of the 40mm grenades.

The final team member carried an M-14 sniper rifle with night vision optics and a bipod.

Rounding out the personal armament of the team were garrotes and particularly wicked SEAL Knife2000 or Applegate-Fairbairn fighting knives, pen lites and an assortment of hand grenades, including percussion, incendiary and AP (anti-personnel).

All armaments were secured with soft velcro closings or in A.L.I.C.E. (all purpose, lightweight, individual, carrying equipment) packs so that no metallic noises would escape during the mission.

The critical equipment of the mission, however, were the two identical kits packaged in hard-sided, water-tight Halliburton cases cushioned on the outside by a matte finish rubber coating and cushioned inside with rigid foam to accommodate the precision instruments and communications devices that they hoped would enable them to defuse and render the nuclear device harmless when they located it. Each kit contained a collapsible satellite phone with encryption, night vision lens, video camera capable of transmitting audio, video and data signals via satellite, and a parabolic microphone eavesdropping system. A variety of small static free hand tools and other devices capable of working on the expected device were included. Identical kits were carried against failure of one kit or loss in a firefight.

Each man was equipped with night vision Xeon goggles and a wireless headset and microphone for close order communications. The optimum range of the system was two clicks.

Despite such weaponry, the mission was intended to be insertion, completion and extraction, not combat.

As luck would have it, the mission got it all. The team's biggest concern on the way in was not Iraqi troops, but sticking to their route to avoid the friendly fire from the missions being flown over Kuwait in preparation for the ground offensive.

Their target destination, based on satellite intelligence as to the most likely site, was only six clicks inland from their insertion point—and they covered the distance in close order within two hours. They were within one half click by four o'clock in the morning. The most difficult part of the trip was avoiding the light of the fires from the burning oil wells.

Crawford sent his two most experienced infiltrators to scout the forward areas for a launch point and to make an assessment of enemy deployment. The remaining members of the team checked their gear and set perimeter watch.

By five a.m. the scouts returned. They had located the probable site and described the forward area. There were four sentry posts walking each compass point. It appeared that they were not communicating electronically and were unconcerned about infiltrators as they were talking and smoking whenever their routes intersected. The camp itself was surrounded by more than one hundred twenty oil storage tanks. The portable military hut that served as the CP (command post), and probable site of the nuclear device, was almost dead center of the storage depot, surrounded by eight massive storage tanks enclosed in an earthen berm covered by crude oil/asphalt to hold the sand in place.

There was only one visible light coming from the redoubt and it was a small window in the hut that probably contained the device and the rest of the crew who would be setting the detonators. Preparations were underway to set the detonators and leave within moments. Little time was left to set up the assault. Their goal was to contain the enemy before the detonators were set and signal an 'all clear' back to their control.

No such luck. The team split into groups of two and each took out one of the sentries without incident. By five thirty a.m. they were ready to assault the hut. Unfortunately, by the time they had secured the crew inside—mostly technical, not warrior types, the detonators were armed. All of those captured were prepared to die in their Jihad or holy war and either did not know, or would not divulge, the instructions for stopping the countdown to detonation.

Feverishly the nuclear technicians on the team began to remove the covers from the operations panels on the device. The communications specialist set up the satellite communications system and the adjunct video camera. Once each procedure was complete, there was a real time link to the Lawrence Livermore Laboratory in California where nuclear weapons' specialists directed the dismantling of the deadly bomb. The countdown had less than two hours left when it was disarmed.

Early Sunday morning, Saudi time, the first shots were fired in the ground war. The First Marine Division crossed over the Kuwaiti border headed toward Kuwait City. By the time they reached the oil tank storage farm they were surprised to see an American flag on top of one of the tanks with eight SEALS sitting on the edge yelling, "It's about time, jarheads. What kept you?"

Kuwait would become a living hell—nine hundred and fifty burning oil wells on fire, along with other widespread destruction and atrocities wrought by retreating Iraqis and allied bombing. On February twenty-eighth President Bush announced victory and ordered a cease-fire.

By mid March, the Emir of Kuwait and the royal family returned to Kuwait City. One of the first things he did was hold a press conference to tout the heroes of the war of liberation of Kuwait. A war photographer accompanying the Marines had taken a picture of Rocko Crawford's SEAL team atop the oil storage tank. The photo became a rallying point for the Kuwaiti's expression of gratitude for the actions of the combined U.N. military force.

The U.S. military, for obvious reasons, was reluctant to identify the team members. But when pressure was brought to bear, Rocko Crawford and his team were awarded the medal of *al Sabah*, the highest award for valor in Kuwait.

The story of the nuclear device and the close brush with destruction averted by the SEAL team's prompt and decisive actions held headlines worldwide for two days. At the White House the President presented a Navy Cross to each member of the team. Secretary of Defense Dick Chaney and General Colin Powell presented unit citations.

Crawford, like Norman Schwarzkopf, became an icon of the Gulf War. But unlike the general, Crawford went back to his work.

Second Defining Moment

"Marriages seldom die suddenly, they usually dissolve slowly from inattention and lack of care. They are only good on purpose."

KEN PEPPER, Ph.D.

Following the election of nineteen ninety-two, before Bill Clinton began his first term, George Bush decided to establish an elite force in addition to Delta Force. Composed of the best of the SEAL teams, no member could serve past age forty. Financial support for the new unit would come from covert funds. The Commander-in-Chief alone had the authority to assign and deploy the unit. Members of this force would be on detached duty status to this assignment. They would train and maintain a DEFCon 4 level of readiness for combat independent of any other military readiness orders. They would be authorized to commandeer any and all resources they needed to maintain this level of readiness.

Known as Strike Force Alpha, members would be career sailors and seasoned combat veterans commanded by no less than a commander, USN. Each would carry a special "get out of jail free" card with explicit instructions to call the Commander-in-Chief in the unlikely event anyone ever impeded his access to materiel, ordinance, transport, communications or intelligence. The cards were seldom displayed and calls to the CIC were never made.

The prevailing fear of the outgoing Bush administration was that a Commander-in-Chief whose only previous military experience had been dodging the draft during the Vietnam War might someday need such an elite force in order to react swiftly to unexpected events worldwide.

So Strike Force Alpha was born.

General Colin Powell recommended that Crawford be tabbed as commander of Strike Force Alpha and petitioned the United States Congress to immediately promote him to the rank of commander, USN.

By Christmas of nineteen ninety-two Crawford had assumed command of Strike Force Alpha and, over the strenuous objections of certain Navy brass hats, declared that Norfolk, Virginia, not San Diego, California, would be the unit's headquarters. The public reason given for the decision was in order to be close to the President. The real reason was so Crawford could continue to live in Virginia Beach.

The selection of the sixteen-member Strike Force Alpha team began in earnest after New Year's Day in nineteen ninety-three. Six members of the team came from the group that had gone to Kuwait with Crawford. The other member of that group had retired from the service after the Gulf War. Nine more men had to be picked, and that process was long and rigorous. It was not until early May that the last man was chosen.

In addition to the normal levels of SEAL performance, members of Strike Force Alpha had to compete on a par with existing members of the team. There were numerous war game simulations in the field that quickly qualified or disqualified would-be and want-to-be candidates. Special consideration was given to language skills, cryptography training, counter insurgency, pilot skills, communications and field medical training.

Of the final sixteen chosen four were proficient in flying fixed wing aircraft. Two had multi-engine ratings and more than two thousand hours of flight time. Three of the men were certified to fly rotary aircraft. One was a flight instructor from Pensacola, Florida who had transferred into SEAL training.

Six were fluent in languages—French, Italian, Spanish, Farsi, Mandarin, Japanese, Vietnamese, German and Russian.

Two were accomplished engine mechanics. If it had a motor, they could make it run and keep it running.

There were five different martial art styles present among the group. All were expert marksmen with every weapon in the SEAL arsenal—and three were armorers. One was an accomplished cryptographer and six were trained in the thirty-week Special Operations medical course specializing in burns, gunshot wounds and trauma (18-D Special Operations Medical Sergeant Course). All were adept at counter insurgency and role camouflage. The youngest was twenty-three and the oldest was Crawford, who was thirty-two.

A red "S" under the SEAL emblem was all that distinguished Strike Force Alpha. It was the only insignia they wore. There were no special berets or colors. They knew they were the elite of the elite and chose to remain relatively anonymous.

During the first Clinton administration elements of Strike Force Alpha were deployed in Haiti, Somalia and Bosnia. That much was known for sure. There was speculation, but no proof that they were also in Eastern Europe, West Africa, Chechnya, the Baltic States and Central America.

Strike Force Alpha helped shape the self-confidence and arrogance of Crawford. He and his fifteen men proved to be an awesome force—and no matter how tough the assignment—they sustained more bumps and bruises training among themselves than they did in combat. Only two of them sustained injuries that required sick bay time and none of them was away from his training regimen more than a week. They were good and knew it. They worked at leaving their arrogance at home when they were on assignment. Unfortunately the place it showed up most often was at home.

Only three of the men remained married, one of whom was Crawford. None, including him, had what would be viewed as successful home lives. They worked hard and they played hard, but seldom did they drink—and then sparingly as a concession to their training and conditioning demands. A notable exception was after a mission's completion when their wardroom resembled a brewery gone berserk.

The vice of choice was often women. Some had a regular sexual outlet. Others, less discriminating, opted for variety.

It had never been all that hard for Crawford to cheat on his wife. Over time it became even easier. And, he had not lost a step in attracting handsome women. By the third defining moment of his life, he had no discernable conscience about the matter.

There was no steady woman in his life, just a steady stream of them. It is a miracle he did not fall prey to every sexually transmitted disease known to man. But selection, so-called safe sex practices, pure dumb luck or some combination of those things kept him free from everything but one case of 'trich' that he hid from Shel until it was safely treated.

•••

The second Clinton administration began amid the hue and cry for campaign contribution reform on the domestic front and relative peace in foreign relations.

Chip was thirteen in nineteen ninety-eight, but knew little of his dad except that he was a warrior often gone from home. He was close to his mother and, despite receiving little attention from either parent, was a model young man.

Chip was fortunate in that he had taken a shine to his Pop Warner football coach, Dewey Youngblood, who had never had children of his own. He and his wife Elise had lived in the same block as the Crawford family since they first arrived at Virginia Beach.

Youngblood taught middle school U.S. history—and Chip was soon spending most of his spare time at the Youngblood residence, coming home only to eat, do homework and sleep. Shel did not notice or seem to care.

Sheldie was at the time a raging tomboy of nine—and a handful. Shel got calls from school almost weekly that Sheldie had flattened some little boy's nose or fallen off something. By age nine, injuries included a broken collarbone and forearm and a total of 11 stitches, If Shel had permitted, her daughter would have cut her hair short as a boy. She was the toughest little kid in the fourth grade.

Crawford was often absent from home. Duty called. Shel retreated further into her work and the onset of her closet alcoholism. Crawford played at the role of husband and father between Navy SEAL assignments punctuated by flurries of inappropriate sexual acting out. Both Crawford and Shel retained a pretense of wholeness for the sake of their parents, but underneath an uneasy air of discontent lay like something rotten.

Third Defining Moment

"Life is either a daring adventure or nothing."
HELEN KELLER

It was apparent in nineteen ninety-nine that the sitting Vice President of the United States was going to make a serious run for the Presidency in the year two thousand. Even before the first caucuses were held behind closed doors, and while the ink was still wet on the ballots in Iowa, the Vice President and his wife had announced to the world that he would be the candidate to succeed Bill Clinton in the White House.

Clinton, of course, endorsed his VP and the major liberal press came out strong for him as well.

The Republicans did not have a strong candidate at the outset. In fact, it appeared that a field of *who's that* and *him again* was going to wage war for the Grand Old Party's nomination in August. Jack Kemp was making a token move, but at sixty-five was a long shot. Elizabeth Dole had left her post as head of the American Red Cross to follow her husband's trail for the Republication nomination. Steve Forbes was set to spend another fifty million dollars of his personal fortune chasing the presidency. John McCain, U.S. Senator from Arizona was a Vietnam Prisoner of War veteran, but a very long shot. Even Dan Quayle was making a run.

Rudy Giuliani, the immensely popular mayor of New York, was a dark horse. Only Governor George W. Bush of Texas seemed to be capable of making a strong run. But no one really stood out in the early going.

Since Bill Clinton had refused to take Ross Perot's suggestion to resign in nineteen ninety-eight, Ross was still pontificating, but fewer and fewer folks took him seriously.

•••

In April of the year two thousand, the Vice President made a trip to Israel to confer with Israeli Prime Minister Ehud Barak and Palestinian leader Yassir Arafat to usher in the next round of Palestinian home rule and peaceful coexistence between Israeli and Palestinian citizens. When Air Force Two landed at Ben Gurion Airport in Tel Aviv it was to signal the start of a VIP reception for the Vice President and his wife. It actually signaled the third defining moment in Crawford's life.

As the plane neared the end of its rollout, the runway behind the plane suddenly erupted as a string of incoming mortar rounds began chewing up the tarmac. As the pilot frantically began to brake and turn onto a taxiway, a helicopter with no markings appeared in front of the plane and began tearing up the tarmac and taxiway ahead of the plane with pod mounted rockets and automatic weapons fire. All the braking power the pilot could muster was not sufficient to prevent the nose gear of the plane from burying itself in one of the craters formed by the barrage on the active taxiway.

The plane lurched to a halt and the nose gear slowly collapsed, setting the nose on the ground. As it slewed to a halt, the primary exit door was facing away from the terminal. Only by Herculean effort was the pilot able to cut the engines before fire broke out.

The Vice Presidential party inside the plane was thrown all over the cabin. By the time the flight crew and onboard Secret Service agents could get to the emergency exits they discovered that only the main doors would open—a fatal mistake. The flexion of the frame of the airliner had wedged the others shut.

During the confusion, the helicopter offloaded a squad of commandos who stormed the plane with grappling hooks. With covering fire from a minigun in the chopper's doorway the commandos burst into the wounded plane at the same moment the crew was able to open the main cabin door.

Three Secret Service agents, a flight attendant and the navigator were killed immediately. Two commandos were shot and one appeared to have been killed.

Six commandos swarmed over the Vice President, holding the rest of the occupants at machine gun point. They bound his arms with duct tape and covered his head with a black cloth bag. Fortunately the Second Lady was in the rear cabin where the door was wedged shut or, as eyewitnesses later testified, they would have taken her, too. Apparently both were targets.

The terrorists deployed the emergency slide and exited the plane. In the process they set off tear gas and smoke grenades. They were picked up on the offside of Air Force Two by the helicopter in which they had arrived. It continued to lay down withering cover fire in the direction of the emergency vehicles that were trying valiantly to get to the downed plane.

One-minute and forty-three seconds after the first mortar round hit the tarmac, the chopper was gone. Only the terrorist who had been killed was left behind. The media described it as one of the most daring and skilled terrorist attacks in modern history.

The helicopter that carried the terrorists was abandoned approximately four miles from the airport. Witnesses said its occupants got into four nondescript Mitsubishi vans and drove away in different directions.

Sheer luck enabled Israeli police to capture one of the vans. The driver, speeding toward the harbor, did not hear the siren of the police car hurrying to set up a roadblock on the harbor highway. The van swerved at the intersection where the two vehicles arrived at the same time and crashed head-on into a concrete loading dock about four feet in height. The driver and front seat passenger were thrown through the windshield. Two others in the rear seat were thrown against the front seats and killed.

The driver was hemorrhaging from a fatal wound to the carotid artery inflicted by a jagged piece of door frame metal. The passenger was relatively unhurt. He was bleeding from numerous cuts and gashes he sustained by what he encountered on his unceremonious exit from the van and from impact with the rough concrete of the loading dock. He was unconscious.

The police quickly called for backup and ambulance assistance. One officer noted that the two in the van were dead. Another officer tried to stem the arterial flow of blood from the carotid artery wound in the driver's neck, but determined it was a losing proposition. The officer who had checked the bodies in the van turned his attention to the other terrorist.

An ambulance and a military police armored personnel carrier arrived and immediately took charge of the wounded terrorist. He was spirited away. The driver bled to death at the scene.

No one knew the condition and whereabouts of the Vice President or his captors.

Within an hour after the Vice President disappeared the Israeli military and units of Mossad were scouring the countryside, closing all borders and chasing down every possible lead. But they could find no trace of the terrorists or the Vice President.

An emergency press conference was called by Bill Clinton and broadcast worldwide. He said: "This morning at Ben Gurion Airport in Tel Aviv, Israel, under the glare of international television cameras, Air Force Two, with Vice President, members of his family and a diplomatic and press contingent aboard, was brutally attacked by armed terrorists. Three Secret Service agents, the navigator of Air Force Two and a flight attendant were shot to death. Their names are being withheld pending notification of next of kin. The Vice President was taken hostage and the terrorists escaped from the scene in a stolen military helicopter. One terrorist has been captured by Israeli military police and is in custody. There is no word on the whereabouts of the Vice President.

"Let me assure you that all the collective resources of the United States government worldwide have been marshaled to bring the Vice President home safely and to bring swift and sudden retribution upon those responsible for this dastardly and cowardly attack on a man of peace."

The President permitted no questions after the announcement.

The vast intelligence network of the United States riveted attention on the Middle East. Satellite intelligence was ordered to intensify scrutiny in an effort to determine how the terrorists managed to get the Vice President out of Israel, if indeed he was out of the country.

The more information that was examined, the more it became apparent that the terrorists involved were not only adept at physical terror, but sophisticated militarists in possession of very advanced intelligence. None of the satellite photos provided useful information. There were ample satellite photos of the end of the attack on Air Force Two. The images persisted until approximately eight minutes after the attack, but for the period immediately prior to the onset of the attack the satellite feeds were in a dark period as surveillance of the region passed from one satellite to another. Thirteen minutes after the attack concluded, the satellites went dark again.

The four vans were located within three hours of the attack. One was abandoned on the road north into Lebanon, one was found along the road from Tel Aviv to Gaza. A third was located in a kibbutz near the Golan Heights. The fourth, of course, was the one that had impaled itself on the concrete loading dock in Tel Aviv.

The three abandoned vehicles had been wiped clean of fingerprints. They were quickly subjected to the best Israeli forensic science available. The van pointed toward Lebanon was the only one found to contain fibers from fabric that matched the suit the Vice President was wearing when he was abducted.

Attention quickly turned to the Bekaa Valley (al Biqa) in Lebanon, long a Mecca for terrorists and where other international hostages such as Terry Waite and John McCarthy had been held undiscovered for years in the nineteen seventies and eighties.

Lebanon, once a garden spot in the Middle East, was still recovering from the civil war that had torn it apart from nineteen seventy-five until nineteen ninety-one. A Syrian mediated and enforced peace agreement finally ended the war, but the area remained strife torn well into the beginning of the twenty-first century.

Situated between the Mediterranean Sea on the West, Syria on the North and East and Israel on the South, Lebanon had been a much-used puck in a deadly game of international hockey. The land had been ravaged and small guerrilla bands of militia were still in control of pockets of the country. The Armed Forces of Lebanon still had to contend with the Israeli backed Army of South Lebanon militia faction and the Syrian supported Hizbollah (Party of God) terrorist brigades.

The geography made it an ideal haven for small terrorist bands. Lebanon is a small country, only two hundred and seventeen kilometers in length and only forty to eighty kilometers in width. It is divided into four distinct regions, west to east. The western edge of the nation sits on a narrow coastal plain bordering the Mediterranean. The capital city of Beirut sits on this plain.

Inland from the coastal plain is the first of two significant north-south mountain ranges—the Lebanon Mountains. This range has the highest point in Lebanon, Qornet Es Sauda at ten thousand one hundred and fifteen feet. The Lebanon Mountains are cut by numerous narrow and deep gorges where it is possible to hide entire guerrilla forces from all but the most direct detection.

The centerpiece of the nation is the fertile Bekaa Valley, where the only navigable rivers in Lebanon provide water for the fields and vineyards that abound. The hydroelectric power for much of the nation is generated in the Bekaa Valley. Never more than fifteen kilometers wide, the valley provides secure hiding places for terrorist groups that can scurry to their redoubts in the mountains on either side. Yet they still have adequate access to food and supplies in the villages along the valley.

The border between Syria and Lebanon is guarded by the Anti-

Lebanon mountain range. Mount Hermon is the highest peak in this range, topping eight thousand feet.

The Bekaa Valley has been a favored location for terrorist camps because of its imposing surroundings, which include many caves and caverns. The presence of many small pockets of well armed guerrilla units has made it extremely difficult to mount any kind of overt traditional military campaign without taking serious casualties. Of course, this condition is magnified when hostage rescue is involved.

The President instructed the keepers of the nation's spy satellites to divert sky-eyes from the Far East and from Central America to stationary positions above the Middle East with specific focus on Lebanon and Syria. As these arrangements were being made, a radio transmission was intercepted in Jerusalem from the group claiming responsibility for the kidnapping.

"Allah be praised, the infidel dog of the Unites States imperialist intruders has been gloriously delivered into the hands of the servants of Allah," the speaker said. "The dog who would be president of the imperialist American republic, will be held by al Fatah Death Brigade until the following list of servants of Allah have been released from the illegal imprisonment they suffer at the hands of the American dogs and the infidels in Germany, Italy and Israel. Death to the infidels."

A lengthy list of nearly three hundred terrorists was then read.

The second demand was for the deposit of one hundred billion in gold bullion in a bank in Zurich known to be friendly to other Arab terrorist groups. The terrorists promised time deadlines and a video within the next two days.

The following two days were relatively quiet in terms of public information, but activity was going at a frantic pace behind the scenes.

The Vice President's wife and the rest of the entourage were brought safely home, accompanying the bodies of those killed in the assault. The spy satellites devoured the ground of the Bekaa Valley and Syria, searching for any movement that might give a hint of the location where the Vice President might be held.

There was little success. It was as though all but two or three suspected terrorist camps in the valley had simply vanished. Even the infrared scans of the area produced limited results.

On the morning of the third day following the abduction, a video was delivered by courier in Tel Aviv to Wolf Blitzer of CNN. It became part of a special worldwide news report.

Dark and fierce Arab eyes could be seen in the openings of a face mask. The voice was perfect Oxford English, but the passion of the Arab terrorist that had become almost commonplace was unmistakable. He identified himself as the commander of the al Fatah Death Brigade. He described his mission as the mother of all holy wars. His sworn intent was to drive the Israeli infidels and their western lackeys out of the sacred lands of his ancestors and to create an Islamic federation throughout all the Middle East. He promised a sanctuary for all victims of western imperialism once they were free from prison.

He repeated the two demands from the previous radio transmission: free the terrorists from prisons in Germany, Italy and Israel, and deposit one hundred billion dollars in gold bullion in certain numbered Swiss bank accounts. Failure to adhere to these demands, he promised, would have disastrous consequences for the Vice President.

Then he shocked a majority of the world's peoples when he said, "We have begun addicting your Vice President to heroin. Within a month he will be a hopeless addict. If the first terrorist releases do not begin within twenty-four hours of the receipt and broadcast of this tape, we will begin sending pieces of the infidel back to you on a daily basis. First, finger joints, then toes, then ears. We will keep him alive as long as we can, but the choices are squarely in your hands. Act now."

The President ordered the carriers *USS Nimitz* and *USS Independence* to the Mediterranean and the guided missile cruiser *USS Dornitz* to the Persian Gulf. SR-71 spy planes joined the satellite surveillance of the region, but little useful information was forthcoming. Every square meter of the Bekaa Valley and the western region of Syria and Jordan was being dissected by satellites and analysts worked feverishly around the clock to interpret the raw data that were pouring in.

Concurrently a team of Israeli Mossad and American forensic scientists were questioning the terrorist who had survived the crash at the Tel Aviv docks. There were no records of his fingerprints with any of the world's major crime agencies. And, his face was not known to any of the world's terrorist watchers. He had no identification and his clothing was standard Israeli military issue, determined to have been part of a cache of arms and uniforms stolen from an Israeli outpost more than three years earlier. Despite application of the latest and most sophisticated techniques and chemically induced motivations, the man would not talk. He was either totally ignorant of any details of the abduction, or was indoctrinated to think that death was his ticket to paradise. Whatever, his interrogators extracted nothing useful from him.

All that was learned was that he and his partners were to rendezvous with a fishing boat and be transported to a larger ship in the Mediterranean. He knew no more, or would tell no more, than that.

The same day the President ordered a beefed up military presence in the region and the deployment of the spy apparatus, he summoned Crawford to the War Room at the White House. Crawford arrived in a plain government vehicle. He was dressed in civilian clothes and wore dark glasses. He looked like one of the secret service guards and was passed discreetly into the War Room.

The Secretary of Defense began the briefing saying, "Commander, the situation regarding the Vice President has not yielded overwhelming intelligence thus far. We have targeted every known terrorist camp in the Bekaa Valley and in southwestern Syria. And, while there is some activity present in the area, it is limited and in numbers too small to represent a significant addition of personnel from our earlier and normal satellite surveillance of the area. Therefore, we are widening our search today to include some of the rugged terrain in the Lebanon and Anti-Lebanon mountain ranges that border the valley.

"Here is what we suspect. If we assume that the Vice President could not have been moved successfully much farther than the Bekaa Valley or the surrounding mountain hideouts, and that is the prevailing sentiment in this room, then the number of terrorists that accompanied him could have been no more than two or three. If that is the case, and since the other terrorists in the attacking force scattered to the winds, it may be that only the two terrorists in the van that had the Vice President aboard are with him.

"We assume that he was drugged and bound, and therefore reasonably easy to transport.

"While we continue to analyze data from all over this region, we are focusing our search in detail on an area triangulated between Bsharre and the Cedars and the Qornet Es Sauda peak. It is some of the most rugged terrain in Lebanon. What we hope to do within a matter of hours is to narrow the possibilities to the most likely and then have you take Strike Force Alpha into the area in a lightning raid. Can it be done?"

Crawford silently looked at the briefing maps and papers before them for almost two minutes. Then he said, "Gentlemen, you find the spot and by this evening we will have a plan to submit. I'll need a briefing package."

Crawford left the White House with his briefing package and returned to the SEAL base at Norfolk. He had already put the team on full combat alert when the news of the terrorist attack was first announced. First things first. What intelligence did they have on the Bsharre - Qornet Es Sauda area of northern Lebanon?

From Bsharre to the Cedars is some of the most spectacular scenery in all of Lebanon. Mountain roads wind through countryside dotted by red-tiled roofs perched precariously on craggy cliffs. Postage stamp sized vineyards and olive groves dot lush valleys.

The mountain town of Bsharre was the birthplace and burial site of Lebanon's most famous artist and author, Gibran Khalil Gibran.

Steeply out of Bsharre the roadway rises more than four hundred meters until it enters the last remnant of the once famous and abundant cedar forests of Lebanon. Some of the remaining four hundred to five hundred trees are more than fifteen hundred years old. They are all that remain from the clear cutting deforestation that harvested the massive trees for the enduring strength and beauty of their timbers. They sit on the slopes of Mount Makmal.

In winter months, the Cedars is a prime ski resort for both downhill and cross-country skiing. In the summer there are still many sightseers, but the crowds are smaller than during the winter ski season. It is a brisk four-hour hike from the Cedars to Lebanon's highest peak, Qornet Es Sauda.

It was this area in which the satellite search was being concentrated. Scores of narrow gorges and switchbacks carved deeply into the landscape were the targets of the search for any signs of activity or infrared detection.

Strike Force Alpha took the available intelligence and began building assault scenarios for the extraction. They considered an amphibious landing north of Tripoli, like the one they made in Kuwait, but discarded it when the possibilities for detection over the several inland routes they considered were determined to be too great.

A helicopter insertion was explored from an Israeli staging point or, alternately, from aboard one of the carriers in the Mediterranean. These, too, were discarded since the possibility for stealth and surprise would be negated by the noise of the helicopters.

Overland routes were considered from a variety of jumping off points, but were each discarded because of the time to target and the possibility of detection en route.

They settled on a HALO (high altitude low opening) jump to the drop zone. Once intelligence pinpointed the most likely site, or sites, where the Vice President might be held, the plan was to drop Strike Force Alpha into the zone under cover of darkness. At least one night prior to the insertion, U.S. and, if possible, United Nations aircraft would fly missions over the Bekaa Valley and the Lebanon Mountains. This would accustom those who might be holding the Vice President to warplanes flying overhead and would provide a covering for the HALO jump the following night.

By the end of the fourth day the outline of the plan was in place. Two probable sites were chosen. Contingencies were made based upon the order of probability of having to move from primary to secondary targets in the event they chose the wrong camp the first time.

On day five the intelligence apparatus was in full motion. Satellite and over-flight data were being gathered and interpreted by hundreds of dedicated career intelligence specialists. Each hoped to provide the key to finding the Vice President alive.

The General Assembly of the United Nations heard an impassioned plea from Madeline Albright, Secretary of State of the United States, for full and unconditional support from all allies and from those who supported the terrorists. She outlined the U.S. plan to beef up all its military might in the region, and the intent of the U.S. and, perhaps, the United Nations to launch surveillance flights over the region. She strongly urged all the nation's allies to join this effort.

However, nothing was heard from the zealots of al Fatah.

On day six the hardware and armaments for Strike Force Alpha were assembled. Each man was equipped almost exactly as the SEAL team had been nearly ten years earlier when they launched the assault on the Kuwaiti oilfields.

There would be two eight man assault teams this time. Each SEAL would have an H&K Mark 23 .45 cal. sidearm (suppressed with infrared laser targeting system). Four members of each team carried the MP5 SMG (submachine gun) with a minimum of ten full magazines each. Each team had two M-16 A3/M4s with M203 40mm grenade launchers attached. Each team member carried 4 grenades. The other two members of each team carried either a SAW or an M-14 (.308 caliber sniper rifle) with flash and sound suppressor, night vision optics and bipod. The armaments were augmented by flash/bang percussion grenades, since this was a rescue mission, not a search and destroy mission. Each team carried an InSat satellite phone and a collapsible parabolic microphone with headset for long distance eavesdropping. Night vision goggles and wireless transmitters/receivers fitted into headsets completed the inventory.

The composition of the team had changed over the years, but not by much. They were slightly older than when first formed. The eldest was still the Commander at thirty-nine years of age. The balance of the team ranged from twenty-five to thirty-six. Nine of the original team were still in service. Two Chinese language specialists—one in Cantonese and the other in Mandarin had been added to the team, and one of the youngest became the third rotary aircraft certified pilot.

Strike Force Alpha had never lost a man in combat. And it would be three years down the road before any of these men took a lethal wound.

Two very different events at the end of day six helped define the mission of Strike Force Alpha. The second video was delivered, and with it a small prescription bottle with a childproof lid. It was delivered by Federal Express to ABC News in New York. The shipping point was Rome, Italy.

The video was not memorable because of the continued diatribe and religious political rhetoric of the terrorists, but because it provided pictures of the Vice President. His left hand was wrapped in a crude towel or bandage from which blood was obviously seeping. The tape showed the Vice President being supported on either side by a terrorist while another injected him with what the video speaker said was heroin. The message was loud and clear. Release the terrorists and deposit the money or welcome the Vice President home one piece at a time. The bottle accompanying the tape contained the tip of a human pinkie finger to the first joint.

The other important event, a full moon, was just beginning to recede over the Middle East.

The day drew to a close with Strike Force Alpha feverishly working to finish the logistics of their plan and to select an insertion point.

The President declined to make a public statement in response to the tape. However, his chief of staff reported that this latest outrage was intolerable and that the full force and weight of the Presidency of the most powerful nation on the earth was being mobilized for a swift and immediate response.

Throughout the night the analysis of the satellite intelligence was refined. By morning the analysts would agree on the two most probable sites based on the current activity at two remote sites near Qornet Es-Sauda. The problem was that either of the two sites could be where the Vice President was being held. They were no more than six kilometers apart. Virtually all activity in these camps was underground, buried deeply in gorges that slashed the mountainsides, and only a minimal amount of outside contact came and went in satellite photos. The normal flow of tourist and commercial traffic in the area made finalizing the strike point even more complex.

The videos had apparently been sent out over a private coaxial network and not carried out by courier from the sites themselves. No external support and supply processes were evident, suggesting that this operation might have been anticipated many months or years in advance of its occurrence.

Strike Force Alpha (SFA) received the intelligence from the analysts in the pre-dawn hours of day seven. After a couple of hours of planning, they decided that it would be best to insert half of SFA, Bravo Team, at a point triangulated between the two camps. Their task, if the first camp was the actual target, was to provide cover and coordinate the withdrawal after the Vice President was rescued. The other half of SFA, Charlie Team, would HALO as close to the primary camp as possible, gather enough battlefield intelligence to launch the strike, and then proceed with the mission.

In the event that the primary site proved to be wrong, Charlie Team would send the message to Bravo Team to move to the secondary site and execute the mission there. Charlie Team would then neutralize the primary site and proceed to the withdrawal staging area to provide cover and extraction support.

It was not the perfect scenario preferred by Crawford, but it was the only way they could manage to provide adequate resources to insure success regardless of which camp contained the Vice President. If neither site was the right choice, Strike Force Alpha would rendezvous at the extraction point and return to its carrier base to await further instructions to launch another strike. No one relished a second insertion since it was not likely that the entire mission could be kept secret from the world if it was not successful on the first sortie.

Weather and insertion and withdrawal details were the next order of business for the men of Strike Force Alpha.

In the meantime a third video and prescription bottle were delivered. The recipient this time was a BBC correspondent in Cairo.

The tape was even worse than the first. The Vice President was shown with both hands bandaged with dirty rags. He was obviously drugged and was shown receiving another injection in the video. The demands remained the same.

In the early hours of day eight final plans for the Strike Force Alpha mission were completed. The team was to be ferried to the deck of the *USS Independence* in the Mediterranean by the close of the day. It was hoped that the mission could be delayed until day ten to provide cloud cover or to allow the waning moon more time to recede. The mission was scheduled to launch under the cover of the continuing over-flights of Lebanon and Syria at one o'clock in the morning on day ten.

This part of the plan was executed flawlessly. SFA was aboard the ship by nightfall, day nine.

The media continued to vacillate between political recriminations and calls for massive retaliation. But no more videos were received by world news organizations.

The team reviewed the battle plan once again. Just prior to midnight on day nine the teams would board two V-22 Osprey aircraft (vertical take off/tilt wing aircraft developed by LTV Corporation) that would ferry them to the drop points at an altitude of seventeen thousand feet.

101

The landing zones (LZs) were precarious. The extraction point, which was the drop zone for Bravo Team, was in a lightly populated watch-pocket sized valley midway between the Cedars and Qornet Es Sauda. It was one of the very few places from which helicopter recovery could be effected. It was nearly two kilometers farther than the geographic center of the two selected sites, but the distance was worth having a secure place from which to extract the teams and, hopefully, the Vice President.

The LZ for Charlie Team was much more dangerous. It called for them to begin their descent at only twelve thousand feet above sea level, which was less than three thousand feet above the target area. To make matters worse, the LZ was not level ground, but the barren side of a mountain with about a fifteen-percent grade and less than a half acre of ground. If a member of the team missed the site they had a chance to be slammed into the side of the mountain or dashed into one of the deep and narrow gorges on either side of the landing zone.

It could not be helped. Any other landing zone would put them too far from the primary site to meet the rigid timetables set for the completion of the mission.

Charlie Team was composed of the best of the HALO jumpers, which included Crawford.

They poured over weather maps and forecasts for wind speeds and directions, anticipated cloud cover and ambient light from the moon. They rehearsed their rendezvous points again and again.

The Israelis had been selected as the extraction force. Since their soil had been violated in the abduction, it was politically expedient that they be involved in the actual rescue. This did not sit well with Crawford, but he was mollified somewhat when the overall command of the mission, including the extraction, was placed in his hands.

As the day drew to a close, it was apparent that there was still going to be more moon than they had hoped for, but there was hope for thin and scattered cloud cover. Regardless, they were going in.

The men of Strike Force Alpha were not told of the fourth video that arrived by courier at the offices of the *Washington Post* just as the evening edition was being put to bed. The demands were taking a more strident tone. The gist of the message was that the imperialist American dogs were not taking the men and women of al Fatah seriously. Therefore, the terrorists would no longer be content to dismantle America's Vice President one joint at a time. Tomorrow it would be a hand, the next day a foot. The message was, "Release the prisoners immediately."

At thirty minutes after midnight the teams were aboard the two V-22 Osprey aircraft and headed toward the drop zones. They were preceded by several waves of A-10 Warthog and F-16 warplanes over-flying the country as a cover for the drop.

At one o'clock in the morning, precisely five kilometers apart, the two SEAL teams exited their aircraft and began the HALO insertions. There was no communication between the teams until all the chutes were deployed at five hundred feet above the ground. The landings were dead on. The teams landed and stowed their chutes. The only injury sustained in the drop was a four-inch gash in the forearm of the communications specialist for Charlie Team. He landed on a hillside, near one of the gorges. His chute caught on an outcropping of rock and he stepped off into the gorge. The lines of his chute and the well anchored rock were all that saved him from plunging several hundred feet down the face of the gorge. At the end of his tether he was slammed against the side of the gorge and struck a jagged rock outcropping with his left arm. The team quickly came to his rescue, hauled him up and bandaged the wound. He was still functional.

Bravo Team, led by Lieutenant Barry Roberts set a perimeter and their satellite communications gear. They were prepared to administer the extraction process or to take the primary roll on the secondary site. A quick reconnoiter did not provide evidence that their presence had been observed.

Charlie Team was not quite as fortunate. They were nearly on top of the primary target site and they were concerned that the slightest movements or sounds might bring swift retaliation.

The men of Charlie Team quickly removed themselves from the plateau and began the slow descent into the gorge where the suspected terrorists might be holding the Vice President. Crawford set up his parabolic microphone and began a concerted sweep of the area listening for voices. When he finally found voice activity he summoned one of the two Arabic language specialists who was assigned to each team.

After listening to the output of the eavesdropping device for a couple of minutes, the specialist frowned and shook his head at Crawford. Apparently this was not the site where the Vice President was being held. To be completely sure, however, it would be necessary to take the camp out, preferably without a firefight. It was preferable not to leave a terrorist behind them who could hinder the extraction once the rescue had been made.

Charlie Team broke into two-man teams and began to encircle the camp. The camp was dug into the side of the gorge, protected by a huge rock overhang. The only visible ingress was between two large rocks that guarded the entrance from below. One of the two-man teams was to find the 'back door' to the bunker and secure it. As the other three teams moved silently into position they listened intently on their headsets for word that the backdoor had been secured. It was approaching two o'clock when a voice whispered, "Back door closed."

The team had crept to within five meters of the rock overhang on the topside of the camp when they smelled tobacco smoke. Seconds later a man stepped out from a rock and relieved himself over the side of a small ledge. The entrance was cleverly hidden.

Re-belting his desert tunic was the last memory the Arab had.

Two sentries were found sleeping near the rock entrance to the redoubt. They never knew what hit them. The night vision goggles enabled the six remaining members of the Charlie Team to enter the hillside dugout silently and swiftly. There were only nine men in the room, all sleeping on mats on the floor. Seven of them died where they lay, and the two who awoke enough to put up any resistance were quickly dispatched.

A cursory examination of the contents of the camp indicated that it was a storage depot with enough arms and munitions to supply several hundred terrorists or guerrilla fighters. Sophisticated communications equipment suggested it was not just a hideout for weekend terrorists.

Time became a formidable enemy almost immediately. Two possibilities occurred to the Charlie Team. If this camp was linked to the secondary site and any communiqué from that site to this one went unanswered, it would alert the terrorists in the secondary camp and they might decide to kill the Vice President. The other unknown was whether or not other terrorists might come to this site before the rescue and extraction were complete and use the weapons and communications gear to alert other unfriendly forces in the area.

They decided to disable the communications gear and booby trap the weapons before leaving the camp. Meanwhile, Crawford's communications specialist contacted Roberts and told him the second site was a go. Charlie Team then completed destruction of the communications gear, set the booby trap charges for the weapons and double-timed the five kilometers to the extraction site in the valley just vacated by Bravo Team. There they set a perimeter and settled down to wait.

The men of Bravo Team found an entirely different scenario at the second site. Under camouflage netting, and dug deeply back into what appeared to be a huge cave in a gorge not quite one hundred feet wide, were six quonset type military buildings. They were approximately forty feet in length. Each hut was capable of holding bunk beds for as many as thirty to forty terrorists. Another structure, like a box, was built so the back wall was the back of the cave. To get to the structure the SEAL team would have to pass all six of the quonset huts going in and coming out. There were also two very wide-awake guards outside the box-like structure.

If the Vice President was being held anywhere on this site, it was likely in the box-like structure.

The improvised plan of attack required additional weapons and personnel from Charlie Team. Roberts quickly relayed that message back to Crawford and half of Charlie Team began the five kilometers march to support Bravo Team. Crawford was one of the four. The wounded communications specialist was left in charge of the remaining extraction team.

Crawford and the other three Charlie Team members each took two additional grenades, giving them a total of twenty-four. When they began their trek it was three-thirty in the morning.

By four-fifteen o'clock Bravo and Charlie Teams were in place. The plan that had been refined during the time it took Charlie Team to reach the second site called for two pen-teams to take out the sentries quietly. As soon as that was accomplished, the pen-teams were to enter the box and rescue the Vice President, if he was there. One of the pen-teams was to stay in the box and defend it and the Vice President at all costs until the remaining ten members of the combined teams secured the huts.

The four M-16 A3/M4-M203 operators were each to have fourteen grenades and responsibility for the six huts. The remaining six team members were to start the assault by simultaneously opening the doors of each hut, throwing in three flash/bang grenades and then running like hell for their positions. The automatic weapons operators would immediately begin launching grenade rounds into each hut as quickly as possible. Any terrorist who emerged from a hut would be cut down by the MP5s, the M-14 or the SAW in the hands of the rest of the team.

And that is just what happened.

When the firefight was over all the terrorists were dead. The Vice President was in the box and was virtually incoherent. He had lost at least thirty pounds in the ten days since his capture and was almost unrecognizable.

The medical specialists quickly cleaned and bandaged his wounds. The terrorists had removed two of his fingers on his left hand and one from his right hand. They had bottled them up in the prescription bottles and had them waiting to send out with subsequent tapes.

The Vice President was unconscious one-minute and the next minute hallucinating. There was no way to know what demons raged through his memory.

The team members quickly did an intelligence sweep, destroyed all remaining communications gear and armaments in the camp, then loaded the Vice President onto a makeshift stretcher and headed toward the extraction site. The going was tough until they cleared the walls of the gorge. As they began trying to raise the remaining members of Charlie Team, they heard the unmistakable sounds of a firefight in the distance.

In less than twenty minutes all of the Strike Force, except the two Charlie Team members who were carrying the Vice President, reached the extraction site and joined the four remaining Charlie Team members who were engaged in a fierce firefight of unknown origin. An estimated terrorist force of fifteen to twenty men was trying to reach the valley floor where team members were dug in. If the SEAL team had not had superior weapons and a nearly perfect defensive perimeter, the terrorists might have overrun their position before the rest of the team showed up.

At almost the same time, two HH60A Night Hawk helicopters from the Israeli army arrived on the scene accompanied by two Apaches AH64 equipped with 19 FFAR rockets, 8 TOW missiles in 2 Quad launchers, an XM 230 chain gun and 23 AIM-9M sidewinder heatseeking missiles They showed up just ten minutes before the Vice President's litter arrived. Between the door gunners on the Night Hawks and the Apaches, the remaining guerrillas were held at bay while the Vice President and all members of the team boarded the Night Hawks.

A ground-to-air shoulder fired Stinger missile took out one of the Apaches, and a fragment from the resulting explosion shattered the windscreen on the lead Night Hawk as it revved its engine just before lift off. The pilot was critically wounded, and the copilot received a severe gash to his right hand that made it impossible for him to operate the aircraft. Amazingly, none of the shrapnel hit the Night Hawk's rotor blades.

Crawford, who was seated directly behind and between the pilot and copilot, managed to grab the controls while two team members extracted the wounded pilots and began battlefield trauma care. Crawford slid

107

into the left seat and assumed control of the damaged helicopter. It did not fly well, but at least it flew, all the way back to the deck of the *USS Independence* off the Lebanese coast.

When the choppers moved out of range of the remaining terrorists, two Israeli Air Force F-16 jets screamed past and obliterated the area with a napalm barrage.

The Vice President was alive, but not well. Other than the gashed arm suffered by the communication's specialist on the HALO landing, Strike Force Alpha suffered only two casualties. A bullet found the fleshy part of the butt of a Bravo Team member in the last firefight, and a ricochet creased the forehead of the youngest member of the Force after he had boarded the extraction helicopter.

Aboard the *USS Independence* the Vice President's condition was thoroughly diagnosed. He had lost three fingers and the wounds had not been dressed or sutured properly. There was concern that he might lose another finger to the infections that affected the adjacent damaged tissues. Three separate surgeries were required before the hands were ready for rehabilitation.

In addition to the massive weight loss of more than three pounds per day during his ordeal, the Vice President experienced virtual shutdown of bladder and bowel functions. Some liver damage had occurred as well. The most damaging problem, however, was the impact of near-fatal doses of heroin injected into him on a daily basis. A man of lesser physical condition might easily have died.

It was decided that the Vice President would stay aboard the *USS Independence* for several days as she steamed through the Mediterranean. Provisions were made for him to sail all the way to Norfolk since that seemed best to the naval surgeons in attendance. The problems that concerned them most in the short term were the terrible withdrawal pains and flashbacks that kept recurring as the impact of the narcotic and, perhaps, designer psychedelics left his system.

Several times a day, the Vice President awoke with screams of agony, partly from the pain associated with the withdrawal and partly from the hallucinogenic demons that played across his mind.

Since none of the terrorists were captured for interrogation, and their spokesman was either killed or absent from the rescue zone, no one could tell whether or not the Vice President had also been subjected to certain hallucinogenic drugs along with the heroin. Blood tests for other substances were inconclusive, but the flashbacks were very real.

Strike Force Alpha stayed with the USS Independence until it steamed into Norfolk and stood by until the Vice President was transferred to Bethesda Naval Hospital for additional surgery and convalescence. One of the cardinal principles of SEAL life was that you never left a man on the field of battle—never. They accorded the Vice President that courtesy as one of their own.

It would be twelve weeks before the Vice President was pronounced fit to resume his duties. When he did present himself to the public again it was July of two thousand. The American public was very sympathetic, but the bloom of his political career had wilted.

Crawford, Roberts and other members of Strike Force Alpha were surprised at the attention they received when they returned home. There was a ticker tape parade. They were entertained at the White House. Crawford, at the insistence of the President, was a guest on numerous talk shows and was repeatedly interviewed by the major news media. There was an offer for a made-for-TV movie. The notoriety was overwhelming.

Fifteen of the warriors were uncomfortable with the attention, but not Crawford. He discovered that he enjoyed the limelight. He was a great guest on a talk show, and was always willing to sign autographs and be interviewed by the print or broadcast media.

Jay Leno was the first to ask Crawford publicly if he ever thought about running for public office. Leno likened him to Dwight Eisenhower and suggested that having a warrior President would do the country good. Even Leno was surprised that his statement received a standing ovation from the Tonight Show audience.

Suddenly there was mindset shift by the American public regarding the presidential candidates who had announced they were running for the office. The Vice President, of course, continued to be the sentimental favorite of the Democrats who had no other viable candidate. The Democrats were pinning their hopes on the sentimental sympathy vote and whatever the Vice President could muster from his lackluster record in the Clinton administration.

There were a few members of the Republican National Committee who leaned toward drafting a forty-year-old hero with no political experience as their standard bearer, but their view was not popular among the Old Guard. The attitude of the Old Guard of the GOP was that Crawford might have paid his dues in combat, but not in the political arena. They figured he would be easy prey for astute, veteran Democrat campaigners. However, public opinion ruled and swayed even the strongest skeptics at the Republican National Convention the last week of August.

•••

"Tell you what, Ryan, let's hit the sack," I said. "These old bones are getting chilly. How about an early breakfast and then I'll tell you the rest of the story?"

"Oh, come on, Pop, let's just go inside where it's warmer," he said. "I'm a night-owl and I'm sleeping in anyway. I'm not ready to quit tonight if you're up to it."

The truth was that I wanted to go to bed, but this seemed like one of those precious teachable moments that might not wait until morning. I did not want to lose the magic.

"Okay, pal, let's go inside. Now, let's see, where was I? Oh yeah, well, after the Tonight Show suggestion by Jay Leno...."

Election 2000

The Democratic National Convention met in Miami in early August. And, after token opposition from Richard Gephart in the primaries, the Vice President easily won the Democrat nomination with eighty-five percent of the primary delegates committed on the first ballot.

The Convention was nothing more than a big pep rally staged for television and the delegates. It was designed to kick-start what had generally been a lackluster campaign. There were lots of questions the American people wanted answered, especially about the ability of the Vice President to govern in light of his ordeal in Lebanon. Privately many wondered if the persistent rumors of flashbacks were true. Was he experiencing flashback episodes from his drugging? Was he capable of governing? Was he garnering only the sympathetic and 'Yellow Dog' votes?

After the Vice President was nominated on the first ballot he surprised everyone by selecting George Stephanopolous, former outspoken chief of staff for Bill Clinton, as his running mate.

The Republicans met in Philadelphia, Pennsylvania, three weeks later. It was the most memorable Republican Convention in modern history.

111

No one came to the Convention with enough committed delegates to win outright on the first ballot. The convention was not going to be a pep rally with a foregone conclusion.

Five people were entered into nomination. The only real blessing was that the frequently painful ordeal of nomination speeches was mercifully shortened to accommodate the vagaries of television scheduling. Rudy Giuliani, mayor of New York City, was nominated by Harold Steward, mayor of Albany, New York. Elizabeth Dole was nominated by her husband, former U.S. Senator, Bob Dole, and Steve Forbes was nominated by Johnson Smithers, governor of Pennsylvania. Dan Quayle, having secured eleven delegates in the primaries was nominated by Don Robert Thomas, junior Senator from Indiana. George W. Bush of Texas was placed in nomination by his father, former President George Bush. All the others had long since withdrawn from the race.

More than six hundred delegates came to the convention, uncommitted. Something was in the wind. Then the balloting process began.

When the roll call for the first ballot began, the spokesperson for the Colorado delegation said, "The great Rocky Mountain State, home of the best downhill and cross-country skiing in the United States, casts its twenty-seven uncommitted votes for the hero of the daring rescue of the Vice President, U.S. Navy Commander—and the next Republican President of the United States—Rockland Hamilton Crawford."

The attendees erupted with a spontaneous ovation.

By the time the U.S. Virgin Islands cast its two votes, it was apparent that there would be at least one more ballot. No candidate had received a majority.

While it is normal for candidates to drop out if they fair poorly on the first ballot, and historically arm-twisting has been used to get the 'also rans' to drop out, it was not to be this day. Every candidate decided to stay in to the bitter end. In the GOP's history, a candidate once stayed in the race for one hundred and eighty-one ballots. Most of the delegates present hoped this would not be one of those days.

First ballot results were: Steve Forbes, one hundred and sixteen votes; Dan Quayle, one hundred and twenty-three votes; Elizabeth Dole, two hundred and twenty-four votes; Rudy Giuliani, three hundred and forty votes; Rocko Crawford, five hundred and seventy-five write in votes; and George Bush, six hundred and twelve votes.

Nine hundred and ninety-six votes were required to win, so after a brief huddle with network television the second ballot was joined with the same candidates who had begun. Of course, none of the delegates was committed on the second ballot. They could simply vote their choice, and a ground swell began to rise.

The moderator began the roll call again as before:

Alabama	40 delegates
Alaska	19 delegates
Arizona	39 delegates
Arkansas	20 delegates
California	163 delegates
Colorado	27 delegates
Connecticut	27 delegates
DC	14 delegates
Delaware	12 delegates
Florida	98 delegates
Georgia	42 delegates
Hawaii	14 delegates
Idaho	23 delegates
Illinois	69 delegates
Indiana	52 delegates
Iowa	27 delegates
Kansas	31 delegates
Kentucky	26 delegates
Louisiana	28 delegates
Maine	15 delegates
Maryland	32 delegates

Massachusetts	37 delegates
Michigan	57 delegates
Minnesota	33 delegates
Missouri	36 delegates
Montana	14 delegates
Nebraska	24 delegates
Nevada	14 delegates
New Hampshire	16 delegates
New Jersey	48 delegates
New Mexico	18 delegates
New York	102 delegates
North Carolina	58 delegates
North Dakota	18 delegates
Ohio	67 delegates
Oklahoma	38 delegates
Oregon	23 delegates
Pennsylvania	73 delegates
Puerto Rico	14 delegates
Rhode Island	16 delegates
South Carolina	37 delegates
South Dakota	18 delegates
Tennessee	37 delegates
Texas	123 delegates
Utah	26 delegates
U.S. Virgin Islands	2 delegates
Vermont	12 delegates
Virginia	53 delegates
Washington	36 delegates
West Virginia	18 delegates
Wisconsin	36 delegates
Wyoming	20 delegates

Paul Sammons, chairman of the Alabama delegation began the trend. When his state was called he said, "Mr. Chairman, the great State of Alabama takes pride in having agreed among ourselves to cast a block vote on this historic second ballot. It is abundantly clear to us that there is a new kind of storm brewing here tonight, and that storm is being led by a bright young U.S. Navy SEAL."

Before he could say another word the delegates broke the instructions of the chair again and burst into cheers. It took several minutes to calm the raucous crowd.

Once the crowd noise was under control Sammons continued saying, "We proudly cast all forty of our votes for the first write in candidate ever to win the Republican nomination and the White House, Rockland Hamilton Crawford."

The final tally gave Crawford one thousand and forty-nine delegate votes. His closest competitor was George W. Bush, who had eight hundred and thirty-nine delegate votes.

As luck would have it, the State of Virginia, Crawford's and Shel's adopted home for nearly twenty years, had the privilege of casting the deciding votes.

Even the commentators ran out of things to say about the celebration that ensued. The demonstration was neither staged nor timed. The mood of the convention was euphoric. There had never been a convention like this. The mood would carry over and become contagious throughout the country during the subsequent presidential campaign.

News pundits had a lot to talk and write about. Many of them, of course, claimed to have predicted this event in the wake of the immense popularity of this young, handsome warrior. Hindsight is ever so clear.

The mood of the nation seemed clear enough, it was that the country had gone soft in foreign affairs. It was an absolute outrage that a sitting Vice President of the nation could be kidnapped in broad daylight while on a diplomatic mission. It must never be allowed to happen again, and a tough young warrior President would not let it happen. There was a renewed interest in taking the war on terrorists to their own turf. And Crawford was the man to do it.

Although a political novice, Crawford was a strong-willed, highly intelligent and well educated man who could adapt to any battlefield—domestic or foreign. He was a quick learner, one who did not make the same mistake twice.

After the overwhelming giddiness of the nomination subsided, Crawford quickly had an acceptance speech crafted for him by Laurence S. Murphy, the preeminent political rhetorist of the Republican Party. He and Shel made a strikingly handsome couple on the dais. Many likened them to the young Jack and Jackie Kennedy. That similarity, of course, was more than just a surface image. The new Presidential nominee was every bit as much a lady's man as John F. Kennedy ever was reputed to be.

To the surprise and delight of convention delegates and the nation, Crawford selected Governor Kristie Whitman as his running mate. She was a savvy veteran political campaigner who had been re-elected governor of New Jersey in nineteen ninety-seven by the narrowest of margins. She was tough and shrewd.

Republicans traditionally raise more campaign money than the Democrats, but with Crawford as their candidate the margin of difference skyrocketed. That difference was further mirrored in November. Crawford won sixty-seven percent of the popular vote and carried every state except Tennessee and Massachusetts.

The inauguration in January of two thousand one not only launched a new century, it ushered in what would become a real revival of common sense in this nation, but that would come later.

The inaugural balls were resplendent with military finery. The newly elected president surprised the nation by showing up in his U.S. Navy Commander's formal dress uniform with ribbons on board, including the four inch gold al Sabah medal from the emir of Kuwait. He was a Navy veteran of twenty-two years, counting his time at Annapolis, and this was the crowning day of all those years.

At each of fourteen official inaugural balls a military honor guard opened the festivities with a silent drill routine. It was a splendid, memorable night that offered no forecast of what was to come.

Crawford selected Barry Roberts as chief of staff, realizing he needed another warrior he could trust in the uncharted waters of Washington politics. It was a good choice for both. Roberts possessed a unique knack for politics and organization.

Strike Force Alpha came under new leadership, but this time it's homeport was transferred to San Diego. The Navy brass finally won that point.

It's a Girl

"All children are born good."

LORD PALMERSON

A strange thing occurred in June of two thousand two. Sheldie was nearly eight months pregnant and the White House staff was collectively holding its breath waiting for the next crisis to occur. If it had not been for the superb work of the staff and the support of Vice President Whitman, the wheels of the executive branch of the federal government might have come to a halt. The eyes of the world were riveted on the soap opera starring the dysfunctional First Family.

During this time six men who normally did not request presidential appointments persisted in requesting an audience with Crawford.

In late June, Florence James had finally had all she could stand. She told the President that hardly a day went by that she did not get one or more calls from Billy Graham, evangelist; Bill Cosby; Bill McCartney; Bill Moyers; Steven Covey and Robert Bly. Each of these men, she told Crawford, said they had an urgent message to share with him.

Because Florence was able to convey the passion of their requests, Crawford instructed her to set up an audience for the men collectively during the first week in July. She scheduled the meeting for July six at Camp David.

119

Four of the six men had met Crawford. He and Graham had met after the Desert Storm heroics. While the two had not become close friends, they did share a respect for each other. They had encountered each other on several different occasions during the nineteen nineties.

Cosby, who had made a rare contribution to Crawford's surprise run for the presidency, had appeared with him on several occasions during the campaign.

McCartney, who had helped found the men's Christian organization called *Promise Keepers*, had inspired the young Crawford with his abilities as a football coach at the University of Colorado. Had he not received an appointment to Annapolis, Crawford had considered attending the University of Colorado. While in High School Crawford had been involved in the Fellowship of Christian Athletes and had met McCartney at a State FCA event.

Moyers had interviewed Crawford in the early nineteen nineties for a PBS television program profiling American heroes of the last half of the twentieth century. The interview had video-chronicled men like Dwight Eisenhower, John Kennedy, Martin Luther King, Jr., and Douglas MacArthur. Live interviews were held with Jimmy Carter, Colin Powell, Norman Schwartzkopf and Crawford.

Covey, CEO of the Franklin Covey Corporation, and made famous by his books and lecture series on *The 7 Basic Habits of Highly Successful People* , *Principle Centered Leadership*, *First Things First*, and *The 7 Basic Habits of Highly Successful Families*, had never met the President.

Nor had Bly, a champion of the process of transformation for men and widely acclaimed as the founder of the men's movement toward self-realization and wholeness.

As would be discovered, each of the six men had experienced something akin to that of the character played by Richard Dreyfuss in the movie *Close Encounters of the Third Kind*. They had been beset by a persistent and intense urge to call the President and offer their sympathies and support during the time of his wife's health crisis and his daughter's pregnancy.

This urge was so consistent and persistent that they were unable to take *no* for an answer.

Not one man knew the sense of urgency of the others until they finally met with the President. Graham, the first to arrive, told Crawford, "I'm not sure why I'm here. I only know that I have the most intense urge I have ever had to be here to lend you my care and support in these trying times."

With that preamble Graham and the President began what would extend to a two-week long encounter that would change Crawford forever.

At noon McCartney arrived and made a declaration nearly identical to the one Graham had made. Initially each thought it coincidental, but then Cosby arrived and said, "I don't know why I'm here. I only know that I've had the most intense urge to be here to lend you my care and support in these trying times."

Graham would later define this event as what some might call "coincidence"—*when God does something miraculous and remains anonymous.*

When Moyers and Bly arrived and said basically the same thing the others had, they were convinced that something beyond human was at work. Then, just as dinner was being cleared from the table, Covey finally arrived. His flight from Salt Lake City had been delayed. Over dessert he was interrupted by gales of laughter when he said, "I don't know why I am here, but..."

Later that evening Crawford asked each of the men if they could stay a few days. None of them realized that a few days would turn into nearly two weeks. Over the course of those days the seven men became inseparable. Crawford spent a few hours each day conducting necessary business, but the balance of his time was spent with one or more of his guests.

Each of the men had a particular message to deliver to the President. It was an incredibly intense time for Crawford. He struggled with each message, at the same time waging war within himself because of

121

the demons of his past. His aberrant behavior—his mistreatment of his wife, his cavalier approach to fatherhood responsibilities and his rampant womanizing—looked glaringly different in the light of his present circumstance.

Night after night, long after his guests had retired, Crawford walked the trails of Camp David, often speaking aloud to himself, often in tears, always in deep remorse. The truth of the old battlefield adage that there are no atheists in foxholes became painfully clear to him on these walks.

His initial remorse was simply embarrassment over being caught and fear that he might lose all that was dear to him—the presidency, his family, his reputation and, surprisingly, his wife. He had not realized how much Shel still meant to him.

The cloying grief was overwhelming. The Secret Service detail that followed him at a distance night after night would later report that even from a distance of several hundred feet they could hear him cursing God and crying aloud, "Why? Why?"

Only one who has experienced the pain of public exposure for misbehavior could know the anguish Crawford was going through. It is one thing to misbehave in the dark where no one sees, but quite another to have that misbehavior overexposed—suicide notes, tabloid headlines, press conferences, the nightly news.

Graham urged Crawford to return to the basic faith with which he had been raised on the prairies of Kansas. Fred and Mary Crawford had faithfully immersed their children in the Christian gospel at the Prairie Congregational Church in Olathe. They were there every Sunday. He had abandoned the faith of his youth and upbringing after arriving at Annapolis. And, it had never been an issue or practice during his marriage to Shel.

Graham spoke to Crawford of David, Bathsheba and the prophet Nathan. Nathan, he said, had told King David an allegory about a rich man who stole the only lamb of one of his poor servants. He had asked David what should be done to this thief who had everything, but stole from his poor neighbor. David said the man should be severely punished. Nathan had then said, "You are that man." David had stolen Bathsheba from her husband Uriah and then had him killed in battle.

In facing the truth about his womanizing, Crawford was forced to face the unpleasant truth that *he was the man* who had, in the vernacular of the day, "screwed the pooch." He had stolen from his wife and family the kind of husband and father they deserved.

Little by little Crawford began the lonely and painful journey toward admission of inappropriate behavior and a budding commitment to change. He would later testify to his family and to the nation, "If anyone had ever told me that I would ever fall down before any entity in the universe and cry in sorrow and repentance, I would have called them a liar."

McCartney's message to the President was wrapped in the seven principles of *Promise Keepers*, the men's movement that had undergone financial crises in the late nineties but had been kept alive by thousands of small groups in churches and synagogues across the country.

The first principle, the former coach told the President, has to do with a man and his God. A Promise Keeper is committed to honoring Jesus Christ through worship, prayer and obedience to God's Word in the power of the Holy Spirit.

"The second," McCartney said, "has to do with a man and his mentors. A Promise Keeper is committed to pursuing vital relationships with a few other men, understanding that he needs brothers to help him keep his promises.

"Then there's the matter of integrity. A Promise Keeper is committed to practicing spiritual, moral, ethical and sexual purity."

The fourth, and one of the most important principles, McCartney told the President, has to do with a man and his family. A Promise Keeper is committed to building strong marriages and families through love, protection and Biblical values.

"And there's the matter of a man and his church," the former coach said. "A Promise Keeper is committed to supporting the mission of his church by honoring and praying for his pastor or priest or rabbi and by actively giving his time and resources.

"There's also the principle of a man and his brothers. A Promise Keeper is committed to reaching beyond any racial and denominational barriers to demonstrate the power of Biblical unity.

"And last, but not least, there's the principle regarding a man and his world. A Promise Keeper is committed to influencing his world being obedient to the Great Commandment, which is about treating all men as brothers, and the Great Commission, which is about taking the message of God to all the world."

At that point Crawford was not prepared to embrace the principles of life outlined by McCartney. But he did recognize that as part of his transformation process and healing such principles should be considered—regardless of the condition of his wife and the outcome of Sheldie's untimely pregnancy.

It was Bill Cosby who won over the President's family, including Rosemary and Sheldie. At first he spent long hours with Rosemary, then with her and Sheldie together. He spoke of the terrible sense of loss that comes when you lose a child and the absolute imperative of making every day special since there were no guarantees that there will be any tomorrows.

Moyers and Bly came in a reprise of their hallmark production for PBS, *A Gathering of Men*, in which they put the men's movement on the map. They were forerunners of the work done by McCartney and *Promise Keepers*. Moyers, a conservative Christian; and Bly, a poet, storyteller and influential author; had joined with a group of men in the early nineteen nineties to explore new meanings of masculinity. Bly's book, *Iron John: A Book About Men*, was on the *New York Times* bestseller list for sixty-two weeks in nineteen ninety-one. He used *Grimm's Fairy Tales* as a vehicle to explore the myths and cultural underpinnings of a distinctly vigorous mode of feeling, a combination of fierceness and tenderness long ago sacrificed to the demands of post industrial revolution society.

Their message to the President was based on *A Gathering of Men*. It was that men need to recover forms of initiation for contemporary males in order to know how to be a man, a need that transcends each generation so that the present generation has an obligation to provide mentors for younger men. The mystique of the transformation process for men was discussed in detail using poetry, song, fairy tales, mythology, psychology and their own life experiences in the exploration of Crawford's deep feelings about himself, his own parents, his wife, his son and daughter and his role in society.

Moyers wrote in his pocket diary, "We are drawn to gatherings like this by a sense of loss, a loss of familiar myths and road maps, but also by a sense of hope. There is something optimistic about the very willingness of men to learn from one another through sharing the confusion over the problems of life."

Covey's message to the President was that it was never too late to build a functional family in a turbulent world—if the family members were willing to do the work. His message was encapsulated within his *The 7 Basic Habits of Highly Effective Families*.

"Be Proactive," he said. "Become an agent of change in your family. And, begin with the end in mind. Develop a family mission statement. Also, put first things first. Make family a priority in a turbulent world."

Covey told Crawford to think win-win, and to learn to move from *me* to *we*.

"Seek first to understand, then to be understood," he said. "Solve family problems through empathic communication. And think synergy...build family unity through celebrating differences. Then you sharpen the saw by renewing the family spirit through traditions."

Covey gave the President an autographed copy of *The 7 Basic Habits of Highly Successful Families* and a copy of the four-tape adjunct audio learning system.

The seven men spent the last four days of their stay with Sheldie and Rosemary in a kind of unconditional support and fellowship that the popular media would have found maudlin, had they gotten wind of it.

125

The President was able to confess to this gathering of friends and family that his life had been out of control. Despite appearances to the contrary, he had been living a lie. He discovered and embraced the notion that he could not change his behavior alone. He sought from among the spiritual and transformation resources at his disposal to find a source outside himself upon which to rely for direction in the healing process. He began the painful process of admitting his failures and asking for forgiveness. He had started the process of becoming a new man.

•••

Shel's comatose condition continued. Crawford was at her bedside at least one day every weekend, usually accompanied by Sheldie. And Shel's mother continued her daily vigil, overseeing the physical therapy that her daughter underwent daily at the hands of the Navy rehab technicians.

The first signs of recovery from the coma occurred on a weekend in late July. Crawford spent that entire weekend with his wife. He held her hand and told her about the progress of Sheldie's pregnancy and about the dramatic changes that were occurring in his life. He wept openly as he described the guts of the transformation process. He told her about the late night terrors he had experienced as he walked the Camp David trails wondering if he were about to lose his family, his sanity, the presidency and the respect of the nation. He told her about crying out in pain and prayer, feeling that nothing he said made any difference at all.

The more he confronted his demons, the more shame and grief he experienced. The remorse was so deep that at first he thought he would die—and later became worse when he feared that he might not. The neat compartments of his life that were once organized into personal, private and public file folders suddenly dissolved into disorientation. Even the earth itself seemed like quicksand from which there was no escape. Nothing made sense any more.

He told Shel that he had come to believe that he could not survive or recover from his despair alone—and in his remorse he begged her to get well so they might rebuild the shattered lives they had created.

Crawford nearly jumped out of his skin when, at the most emotional point of his confession, Shel suddenly stirred, opened her eyes and looked at him solemnly for nearly a minute before lapsing back into the coma. He almost crushed the call button as he summoned the doctors, nurses, Sheldie, Rosie and Ellen Haverford. But there would be no further movement that day.

Dr. Watson cautioned that Shel's momentary stirring might be a false signal of hope, but Crawford, Sheldie and Ellen would not hear it. Nothing dimmed their optimism. For the first time since learning Shel was in a coma, they began to harbor real hope for her recovery.

Rosemary and Sheldie finally decided nothing more was likely to occur that day and left the room for an examination of the baby, due within the month, leaving Crawford alone with Ellen Haverford and Shel for the first time since the crisis had begun.

Starting a conversation with Ellen had never been easy for Crawford. She had always taken a backseat to her husband in conversing with him—and the events surrounding her daughter's coma had not made conversations any easier. Her usual reserve had been heightened by the distrust she had for her son-in-law whom she held personally responsible for the condition of her daughter. He felt as he had that first night when he met Shel's parents. Words were hard to come by, and this time Shelby was not going to float into the room to rescue him.

"Ellen...Mimi, I must...I need to talk to you," he said. "So much has happened in the past two weeks that I want to tell you about." Ellen continued to hold her daughter's hand and stare at her comatose face.

"Mimi, when Shel opened her eyes this morning, it was while I was telling her what I want you to hear, too," he said. "Please let me tell you what is going on with me."

Ellen turned slightly toward Crawford and nodded her head affirmatively, but her expression never changed.

His words came in a rush—how Shel's attempted suicide and Sheldie's pregnancy had brought every sordid facet of each of their lives into perfect focus; how everything that had seemed important had suddenly paled into insignificance compared to his wife and family; how Moyers, McCartney, Graham, Bly, Covey and Cosby had been directed to bring him to his knees; how he had confessed his shortcomings to Shel and begged her forgiveness; how he had told Shel about Sheldie's decision to have the baby; how he wanted to consider raising the child; and how much he wanted Ellen and Ham to forgive him for being such a horse's ass.

Tears began to flow down Ellen's cheeks. She held up one hand, made a small fist and struck Rocko in the chest with the side of it. Then she began to cry harder. "Oh, Rocko, why did it have to come to this before you came to your senses?" she asked. "Now my baby may never know. God, how I have hated you. It was easier to hate you when you were a jerk."

Then he joined her in crying and they hugged each other. Shel stirred again and whispered, "Mommy."

When Crawford summoned the nurses it was obvious that he and Ellen had been crying. The nurses, of course, thought it was because Shel had spoken.

Rosemary and Sheldie returned from the prenatal exam just after Shel had stirred and called for her mother. Although she had not awakened further, it was a dramatic family reunion for the four of them. Rosemary even softened her hard-nosed opinion of her little brother as he told her what had gone on while Sheldie was being examined.

•••

"Ryan, I wish I could tell you that the First Lady came out of her coma that day," I told my grandson, "but it didn't happen that way. The awakening from her coma would not come until Sheldie returned to the hospital for the birth of her baby. She continued to have short spells when she awoke and asked for her mother or Rocko before going back under."

•••

Sheldie's doctor projected her due date to be August second. She had gained nineteen pounds. If she went beyond August fifth he planned to induce labor.

Sheldie had asked the doctor to keep the sex of the baby from her. She wanted to be surprised.

The last week of July was filled with preparation to transfer Sheldie to Bethesda at the proper time. Considerable time was spent going over baby names, but everyone kept avoiding the real question, which was what to do about the baby.

Finally Crawford and his daughter sat down one evening about bedtime for *the talk*. He said, "Honey, I have a suggestion about our baby." He patted her round belly when he said *our baby*. He continued, "I don't think I could bear to have this little child go away from us just because his..."

Sheldie interrupted with a giggle and said, "Or her."

He laughed. "Okay, *or her* parents got the order of business confused. Frankly, if your Mommy were able to do so I think she would agree, so I want to offer you a gift from us. If you want we will take this little child as one of our own. You can have as much involvement in raising the baby as you want, but we will take any or all of the parental responsibilities as though this baby was one we made together."

"Oh, Daddy," she said, "I do want this baby, but just not now. I've thought about it and I don't want to marry Eric or anybody else right now. I'm not through being a kid yet."

Crawford shrugged. "Okay, but if you ever decide differently I'd be happy to adopt the baby myself. How about that? And, what about Eric? How do you two feel about him being involved in the life of his child? Have you talked to him about it?"

"Yes," she said, "and we decided that he should either have some responsibility and know his child, or else just sign away all his parental rights...if you can do that. I told him we didn't need his money, but when I was mad at him I told him that he should take some responsibility since I'm doing all the work."

"What do you want, darling little mommy."

Sheldie smiled at the pet name her father had been calling her since the first time she felt the baby move inside her. "Could we just get this child out of me and into the world before we decide any more?" she asked. "Just knowing that we won't be giving this child away…and that I can still be at least partly a kid for a little longer…is about all I can handle now."

"Okay," he replied, "but do you mind if I have a chat with Eric? I'd like to tell him what we discussed. And, if he doesn't object, we'll get him to sign away his parental rights to us."

"All right, Daddy, but be nice."

Crawford kissed the forehead of his daughter, whom he considered an amazing child, and tucked the covers in around her. Soon he would be doing the same for her child. He would be a granddad or dad—maybe both.

Later that day Crawford had his attorney draw up an unusual document describing the relationship suggested by his conversation with Sheldie. It placed the decisions about Eric's involvement in the life of the baby completely in the hands of Sheldie and her parents. Eric would have no financial or parental responsibility for the baby.

The President had been having conversations with Georgia Davenport about the baby—and while she was more than willing to shoulder some of the responsibility for her son, she was persuaded to allow Crawford the solution he proposed. He was grateful and she was relieved. He had the document delivered to her and she had Eric execute it. They would have no involvement with or responsibility for the child. They swore never to divulge their relationship without express written permission from Sheldie or her legal guardians. They might see the child occasionally, but only as friends of the family.

That, at least, covers the legal issues, Crawford thought. *Now if only Shel were here…*

•••

Rosemary awakened Crawford in the middle of the night on August first. Sheldie was having contractions and they were close enough to warrant the trip to the hospital. *Marine One* was standing by. Within minutes the medical staff at Bethesda was alerted and the President, Sheldie and Rosemary were on their way.

When they touched down, the preparations to get Sheldie to labor and delivery were completed so quickly and without fanfare that the news media were caught completely off guard. She entered the hospital as just another new mom.

By the time Sheldie was settled in a labor room Rosemary was in her scrubs, Harold Watson at her side. Though Dr. Watson was not accustomed to delivering babies, Rosemary was quite experienced. The doctor had agreed to assist her and had a number of specialists standing by should there be any complications.

Despite her age Sheldie handled the pregnancy like a veteran. When she had dilated the specified amount she was given an epidural to ease the pain. Within forty minutes she was wheeled into the delivery suite— and fifteen minutes later Rosemary announced, "It's a girl."

The baby, twenty and a half inches long, weighed six pounds fourteen ounces.

Crawford was the first to hold her, his eyes wet with tears of gratitude. He had been terrified that punishment for his behavior might have caused this child to be less than perfect, but here she was—a perfect child. *Shoot*, he thought, *child of my baby…I'm a grandpa.* He gently handed the baby to Ellen and said, "Mimi, you are absolutely too young to be a great grandmother. Congratulations."

The new mom was still groggy from the epidural and the exertion of childbirth, but also wanted to hold the baby. Holding the child she said, "Ladies and gentlemen, let me introduce you to Roshelle Crawford."

She explained that the baby was named after her Aunt Rosemary, her mother, Shel, and maternal grandmother, Ellen. She had borrowed letters from each of their names.

The celebration concluded at four fifty-three a.m., August first, two thousand two. The Crawford White House would never be the same.

With the arrival of the morning sun the baby was placed in the nursery. Crawford and Ellen then went back to the suite where Shel had been for the past ninety-nine days. She was obviously sleeping and so

131

they simply whispered the good news to her and then retired to the VIP suites they occupied when at the hospital to begin calling the rest of the family to announce the birth.

However, the rest of the morning held more promise than either expected.

Wake Up Call for a Nation

"We all have big chances in our lives that are more or less a second chance."

HARRISON FORD

The President and his family—Shel, Sheldie, Roshelle, and Rosemary—moved back into the White House on August sixth. Baby Roshelle was almost a week old. Rosemary had agreed to move in for a while to serve as the baby's nurse and to supervise Sheldie's recovery.

The press was present in record numbers when *Marine One* touched down on the White House lawn at eleven a.m. Many pictures were snapped as the family made its way from the landing pad to the White House entrance. No one in the President's family paused long enough to make a statement to the press. It was a toss up as to whether the surprise presence of the First Lady or baby Roshelle caused the most stir.

Dee Gombac had a prepared statement that she delivered to the press corps promising a major statement from the President within the next twenty-four hours. What the press had not gotten wind of was the presentation of Ms. Roshelle Crawford to her grandmother cum mother, Shelby Denise Crawford.

•••

On August second, Sheldie, Crawford, Ellen and Rosemary had gone to Shel's room at Bethesda to present the new baby to her. Sheldie entered the room first and carefully laid the baby on her mother's chest. She said, "Mom, here is my baby. I wish you would wake up and see how beautiful she is. We named her for you and Aunt Rosemary and Mimi. Her name is Roshelle. Please wake up."

The simple faith of a fourteen-year-old mother seemed to do more than medical science had been able to accomplish. Shel suddenly opened her eyes. She was disoriented and groggy, but it was obvious that she was awake. As she began to focus on those in the room she began to cry. She was not alone.

Crawford hugged his wife and said, "Oh, Shelly, I can't believe you're awake. Please don't leave us again. I don't think I can make it without you. It's so good to have you back."

They all began talking at once. Sheldie began telling her mother about her decision to keep the baby. Rosemary was calling for a nurse. And Ellen kept repeating over and over, "Oh my baby, my baby."

Then Shelby cleared her throat, slowly moistened her lips with her tongue and spoke softly, "Somehow I've known all of you were here for a long time. I've heard all of you, although I don't know how. Tell me again so I can know whether what I dreamed is so."

Sheldie showed her mother the new baby. None of her earlier surliness was present. She was just a little girl, still trapped in a woman's body, but with a child of her own.

Shelby held the baby until she grew tired. Rosemary took the baby and stood by.

Shel turned to her husband and asked, "Oh, Rocko, is it true what I dreamed about you?"

He timidly came up on the left side of her bed, pursed his lips, took a deep breath and with a tremble in his voice began, "Honey, I've been a colossal jerk for lots of years, but I've been begging for forgiveness and for a second chance. I'm a long way from being what I want to be, but I'm committed to becoming a good husband and father. I can't wait to tell you what is going on with me. I've even told Sheldie that if you will help me, we will raise this new little darling girl as our own. I can't stand the thought of anybody else doing that."

Shelby began to cry and said, "Then it is true. I didn't just dream that you were here. I heard you cry and heard you telling me what you have been going through. I want to hear it all again. I'm so sorry I put all of you through this. Life had just gotten too heavy for me to carry and I wanted to die, but seeing all of you here I'm glad I wasn't very good at it."

The family agreed that they would keep Shel's awakening a secret, get the family back into the White House and then announce it during a press conference in a couple of days. They made their farewells to the medical staff—then Crawford and Shel spent the last few moments at the hospital alone. It may have been the most genuine and tender expression of love they had ever shared.

Crawford made arrangements with Dr. Watson, barring complications, to have Shel transferred to the White House by the end of the week. If her continuing convalescence required nothing more than Rosemary could handle, they all felt that having the family at home was the best prescription for her.

Watson's team of specialists determined that Shel had sustained no permanent damage from her attempted overdose and, that as soon as she could take nourishment on her own and have a normal elimination cycle, she could go home. It took three days. Watson would later report to a press conference at Bethesda that it was nothing short of a miracle that Shel showed no outward effects from her near fatal coma. Apart from a loss of physical vigor that would only be restored by regular exercise, she was fit to resume her life.

Shel Crawford's regaining of consciousness was heralded to the press on August fifth. She went home the next day.

The nation was all ears for the promised news conference. In preparation for the conference the President invited his parents and in-laws to come to the White House. He also sent word through the Secret Service to bring Chip home from the wheat harvests. He wanted to be surrounded by his entire family when he faced the nation.

He also invited the *six wise men* who had helped launch the processes of change in his life to be present for what would become the most watched news conference in the history of the American Republic.

•••

The news conference was scheduled for the south lawn of the White House on August seventh. Press corps passes were the hottest tickets in town. Every major news service and all the major broadcast networks were represented.

Barry Roberts announced the press conference with the traditional words, "Ladies and gentlemen, the President of the United States."

Crawford strode confidently to the podium. The old spring was in his step and the warrior's steely glint was in his eye. Before speaking he motioned for Shel to be escorted to a place near him. She was followed by Ham and Ellen Haverford, Fred and Mary Crawford, Chip, Rosemary, Bill McCartney, Bill Cosby, Bill Moyers, Robert Bly, Steven Covey and Billy Graham. Only Sheldie was missing from the family circle.

With his winning smile Crawford stared into the cameras and said, "Fellow Americans, I have done you a great disservice as your President these past four months. You have a right to an explanation. The explanation will be lengthy, because there is much to tell.

"First, I have been a lousy husband and father for a long time now. Many of the rumors you have heard about me are true. Casual and inappropriate sex has been a part of my life for a long time…and that…in part…led my precious wife to a desperate act as she sought to rid herself of the demons I helped create. I don't know all I need to know about how to do this, but I have made a firm commitment to become a much better husband and father. I'm tackling this job just one day at a time, and with the help of my family and my renewed faith, I will succeed.

"During my voluntary isolation from you and the nation, my family has undergone the most dramatic changes we have ever experienced. We have suffered much, done some very inappropriate things, and agonized over what we must do now and in the future. There is no way I could possibly stand before you today without the support and strength of my lovely bride. I owe her such a great debt for forcing me to face down my demons. I have never loved my wife more, nor been more proud of her, than I am now. Shelby, please come stand beside me."

Shelby stepped slowly to the podium and slipped her arm around her husband's waist.

"We…I almost lost this lovely lady," the President said. "The pressures of being married to me…and having to pretend everything was all right in our home…were almost too much. God has been gracious in giving us a second chance to do things right. I have never been more proud to stand before you with Dr. Haverford at my side than I am today."

Turning to Shelby he said, "I have loved you from the first moment I laid eyes on you when I was a Navy Plebe at Annapolis. You're the greatest gift and blessing I have ever received in life. I haven't appreciated the gift as much as I should, but by the grace of God and your patience those days are over. I love you very much, Shel, and I promise before God and all these assembled witnesses to spend the rest of my life lavishing you with loving actions from the bottom of my heart.

"And to Ham Haverford and Ellen…who have become *Pop* and *Mimi* to us…I hope you can forgive me for the contributions I have made to this mess. I know of no two people on earth for whom I have more respect, nor from whom I more want forgiveness and the right to earn that respect in the future. Thank you for all the support you gave Shelby during the awful days we recently experienced. During the long weeks of voluntary isolation at Camp David, there were many days that I despaired of your wanting to ever stand by my side again.

Turning toward the six men who had been with him at Camp David, the President continued, "A gift sent to me during those days came…in a sense…in six parts. I'm referring to six friends I now call the *six wise men*…three more than were in the original cast. They're with me here today…Bill McCartney, Billy Graham, Steven Covey, Bill Moyers, Robert Bly and Bill Cosby.

137

"Each of these men came to me at Camp David with a persistence that would make a used car salesman blush. They were told again and again that I was not receiving visitors, but they insisted until Florence James decided to share their requests for an audience with me. For reasons that are not clear even today, I relented and they came.

"With their guidance I faced the inner demons of my life and made a commitment to return to the basic faith that I first learned as a child on the Kansas prairie. I've begged for forgiveness for my inappropriate behavior and am still working on forgiving myself. I have stood over the bed of my wife and wept until I had no more tears, begging her forgiveness. Indeed, part of what Shel may tell you shortly is that even in her comatose state, she knew I was there and that I was making amends for the ugly parts of the past I created.

"The second part of these past four months has been spent taking care of our fourteen-year-old daughter. Sheldie has been both our pride and our despair. A budding teenager trapped in a grown woman's body without benefit of healthy or actively present parents is a prime candidate for all sorts of things. In her case it was an unexpected and unwanted pregnancy.

"I wish Shel had been with me during the months I dealt with our daughter's pregnancy, but since she wasn't I'm grateful that my big sister Rosemary was. Rosie, you are the best. I'm sorry we have not been closer in the past, but those days are over. I love you...and I could not have managed this time without you."

Rosemary began to weep and the President continued.

"When Shel found out that Sheldie was pregnant, she could no longer cope with the charade that our lives had become. We were fortunate that we found Shel in time or we might have lost her forever.

"That was when I decided that I needed relief from Washington's press corps. Hopefully you won't take offense," he said, smiling, "but you are nothing if not persistent. So we elected the seclusion of Camp David. Forgive me for keeping you in the dark these months, but I simply did not have the answers you were looking for. We had to go away and, as much as it sounds like a sound bite, we had to find ourselves first.

"I really came to know my daughter these past four months. She and I have struggled with what to do about this unexpected intruder in our home. We explored all the options, including a late term abortion, but Sheldie exhibited lots of maturity in this matter.

"Therefore, after weeks of deliberation, we decided that Sheldie would carry this child to term and we will keep this child in our family. Shel and I have agreed to raise Sheldie's child as one of our own.

"Sheldie, please come present Miss Roshelle Crawford to the world."

Sheldie came slowly through a door to the left of the President. She was carrying her baby, wrapped in a soft summer weight blanket, wearing a pink jump suit with a ribbon taped to her nearly bald blonde head. She handed the baby to Crawford and stood beside him opposite her mother.

"Chip, come join us, son, The President said. "This affects you, too."

Chip strode up beside his Dad and they put their arms around each other. The President hugged his son and they exchanged smiles. Rocko paused a moment before continuing to recall the night in the middle of May when he and Chip sat outside the family residence at Camp David and discussed man-to-man what was happening in their family. He recalled the joy and pride that he had in his son that night as he risked opening his heart to this man-child at his side.

Chip was surprisingly mature in acknowledging that he suspected the problems his parents had, and loved them anyway. When Rocko expressed shock that Chip knew anything about his womanizing and his mother's alcoholism, Chip matter-of-factly stated that kids usually know or suspect more than their parents ever think they do.

They had cried a little together and sat then, as now, arm in arm. Rocko had never been prouder of his son.

It was Chip's idea to join his grandfather's wheat harvest for the rest of the summer. He told Rocko that he would stay if he needed him, but his choice was to just get away until there was some change in his mother.

Now as Rocko looked at the work hardened, sun tanned young hard body standing tall next to him, he silently thanked God again for giving him the privilege of having this fine young man as his son. He would never again take for granted the responsibility of being a dad.

The Crawford family stood together admiring Roshelle for several moments before Crawford spoke again. His voice broke as he said, "Ladies and gentlemen, my fellow Americans, this little girl did not ask to be here, but she is. She is here, in part, because Shel and I did not give Sheldie enough grounding on what is important and what isn't. That's our fault, and we will live out the rest of our lives helping make her place in the world a better place to be. Shel and I have decided to take Roshelle into our home as our own child. We will work hard to help Sheldie salvage what is left of her childhood without sacrificing her child in the process. We are not sure this is the most right thing to do…and it might not be the right thing for every family in our circumstance…but it is right for us.

"There are thousands of Sheldies and Roshelles in our country today. There will be thousands more if we do not put an end to the madness that encourages teenage sex, that brings children into this world prematurely, that does not value or vigorously promote preparation to become husbands and wives and mothers and daddies. It takes more effort to become licensed to drive a car than it does to become a spouse or a parent. This has to end."

The President held Roshelle aloft for the cameras and said, "I am committed…as your President…that no other little child in this country will ever have to grow up without opportunity for training and encouragement in the skills required to create healthy homes and families. This commitment *will be* the defining principle upon which I will build the balance of my presidency and my life."

He kissed Roshelle on the cheek and said, "I love you, little darling," and handed her back to Sheldie. Shel and Sheldie and Chip stepped back from the podium as the President opened the floor for questions.

"Mr. President, Ted Thomas, *CNN*. When will we meet the father of this child?"

"Ted, as far as we're concerned, you won't," Crawford replied. "Had we elected to place this child for adoption, or if we had simply adopted this baby, you would not even consider the question. You and any others who care would simply celebrate the presence of a new life in our home. I encourage you all to lift the level of your questions and join us in doing the same kind of celebration. The young man has a right to get on with his life as well. We have a suitable arrangement with him for handling his responsibilities. He only wants the best for Roshelle and we for him. We will not address this question or any like it again. Thank you for getting this issue on the table early."

"Mr. President, Shirley Moore, *US News & World Report*. I wonder if you would comment further about the word that has been used to describe your marriage...the word *charade* and this *rebirth* you mentioned."

The President nodded in the affirmative and said, "You've all heard the storybook side of our lives...how Shel and I fell in love while I was at Annapolis and she was an adjunct professor on loan from MIT. You've also heard how our lives bloomed...hers in quantum physics and nuclear power followed by motherhood...mine as a Navy SEAL capped by a whirlwind ride to the White House.

"But the public story was a charade. We did not have a bad marriage...it just wasn't a good one. We kept up appearances but inside Shel and I both fought serious dysfunctional disorders...her demon of choice became alcohol and mine was sex.

"The truth...as we are beginning to understand it...is that we have really been blessed by the circumstances that have occurred to us within the past one hundred and ten days. If Sheldie's condition had not come to Shel's attention...and if her own dramatic action that followed had not occurred...we might never have reclaimed the zest for life and started the process of living a healthy lifestyle that characterizes our family today. I hate how we got here, but I would not trade what we are gain-ing as family and personally for anything in the world…even the Presidency.

"I owe a lot to these six familiar faces behind me. As previously stated, our family calls them the *six wise men.* Collectively they carried messages we needed to hear. As Billy Graham so eloquently put it, our getting together was no mere coincidence, unless you define coincidence as he did…*when God does something miraculous and remains anonymous.*

"Shel, our parents and our children…all three of them…have asked Bill Moyers, Robert Bly, Bill McCartney, Bill Cosby, Steven Covey and Billy Graham to join us in what we believe to be the single greatest challenge of the twenty-first century. That challenge is to build healthier families into which to birth and rear children.

"That, Shirley, may be more than you asked for."

"Mr. President," Moore said, "a follow on question, if you please. May I address this to your wife?"

He shrugged and replied, "You've been around my wife enough to know she always speaks her own mind. And, no, I don't mind your addressing her." Then with a pointed finger and faux sternness he said, "Just be nice."

"Is there any more you want to tell us about the events of these past several months?" Moore asked the First Lady.

Shel turned, patted her husband on the arm and stepped smartly to the podium. "Shirley, I have more to say than you have time to hear. And perhaps that will be something we can do later in more detail, but let me describe for you the metamorphosis that I have observed in our family.

"When I first overheard that Sheldie was pregnant, all the pent-up rage and resentment of the past years sprang up at once…and the insidious demon of alcoholism reared its ugly head and won me over. I simply did not have enough emotional prowess to continue what Rocko described as the charade of our lives. It was an easier choice to lose myself completely in the addiction than to face the unpleasant realities of home.

"I will ever be grateful to our good friend Mal Willingham of the *Post,* without whose timely intervention I would no doubt have died. Thank you, Mal." Shel began to applaud the reporter and everyone joined in.

Willingham stood and bowed slightly to the First Lady. He smiled. There were tears in his eyes.

"Oddly enough," Shel continued, "the real healing came for me while I was in the coma. Many days I was aware of what was going on around me. I remember my mother being there often. I remember when my dad came once. I remember Sheldie being there and talking about her dad and about being scared and about Rosemary.

"Rosie, you have been the mother to my darling daughter that I should have been during these days, and I will ever be in your debt. Thank you.

"I'm going to save the best till the last, but before I do, there is one more relationship that I want to make sure is restored here. Daddy, have you and my husband kissed and made up?"

Both Ham Haverford and Crawford were caught by surprise. Neither had spoken to the other since Shel had awakened from the coma. Their discomfort with each other was apparent to all. The President sighed visibly, squared his shoulders, and made a move toward Ham. The reporters chuckled as the President sighed again and held out his hand awkwardly in greeting to Ham. Ham did not budge or change expression until Ellen nudged her husband in the ribs. There was a collective in-drawing of breath as the crowd waited for the outcome of this encounter. After what seemed like an eternity, the older statesman smiled and slipped past the outstretched hand of his son-in-law and gave him a hug, which ended with both of them slapping each other on the back in a display of genuine affection.

Shel turned back to the bank of microphones and continued, "Now that's more like it. Everyday while my mother was helping me exercise in bed, she talked to me about her fears that daddy would never forgive Rocko and that she might lose their grandbabies if I didn't recover. I just wanted to be sure."

This time the assembled press corps burst into spontaneous applause.

She held up her hand for quiet, and her face turned somber. "The best gift, however, was the day long visit with my husband just before

Roshelle was born. Rocko had apparently had the visit with the *six wise men* and had experienced the transformation he has described.

"In the privacy of my hospital suite, with just the two of us present, he cried like a baby. I don't remember him ever doing that before. He told me of his deep sorrow for his contributions to our *charade* of a marriage, begged me to forgive him and invited me to begin again as his bride. I'm not exactly sure about this next memory, but I recall him placing my wedding ring back on my finger and asking me to marry him again.

"I was surprised that the nightmares that had floated in and out of my subconscious state seemed to disappear after that...and there was a tranquillity about my rest that I cannot describe. I felt like I had been reborn...or had been reinvented...or had had a complete overhaul with all new parts. It was the most peaceful feeling I have ever experienced.

"Now that I am awake and the President...no, not the President, just Rocko...and I have had a chance to examine our responses to each other and to our children, the feeling that we have a real chance to begin all over again is even more pronounced. We still have lots of work to do in unlearning some awfully bad habits, but we are committed to getting the job done. I don't like how we got here, either, but I'm surely glad we did. I feel like a bride all over again.

"Finally, the one nice thing about being comatose all these weeks is that I was able to complete the detox protocol without the unpleasant side effects of knowing what was going on. Today I am clean and sober. And I have committed...one day at a time...to a regimen of diet, faith, study, exercise and support that I am confident will keep me that way. You may never have witnessed such a health conscious President and First Lady in this city.

"Thank you all for your prayers, cards, flowers and support during these past days. And now, just one more request...would you, after this day is done, allow us to begin focusing on the future and not on the past. We can undo nothing that is behind us, but we can change the present and the future. We are counting on you to raise the bar in reporting news about us from here on, focusing on what we can and must do to keep other American families from ever having to go through what we have just endured. The odds of others being as fortunate as we have been are way too long. Let this day serve as a *wake up call* for the future. Thank you."

Several more questions were posed, some attempting to dig more deeply into the First Family's past, but they were turned aside without comment. Surprisingly, with admissions of past indiscretions confessed, there would not follow a constant string of investigations and explanations of plausible deniability that had characterized former Presidents like Franklin D. Roosevelt, Eisenhower, Kennedy, Nixon and Clinton.

The President closed the news conference by announcing the formation of a Presidential Commission on Families to examine the causes of family dysfunction and to prescribe a plan of action for the twenty-first century and beyond.

The First Family retired to the White House to reacquaint themselves with each other and to become better acquainted with Miss Roshelle Crawford.

Nothing much happened until after Labor Day. The President resumed his office schedule, Ham and Ellen returned to Boston, Fred and Mary returned to Kansas and Chip returned to school. Shel decided that her teaching experience would allow her to make crash course preparations to home school Sheldie for at least a year. Rosemary agreed to stay on until Christmas.

The First Lady was serious about remaining clean and sober. She sent personal notes to Washington insiders who frequented the White House—legislators, cabinet members, senior military officers and their collective spouses. Shel invited any and all of them who might be struggling with alcohol abuse or recovering alcoholics to join her in a Capitol Hill peer support group.

She was overwhelmed by the response. She received more than sixty follow up calls and letters to her personal notes. Some applauded her efforts and to her surprise, nearly forty people expressed interest in joining such a group. The upshot of the matter was that a Capitol Hill support group was formed to foster twelve step work and mutual encouragement. The first meeting on the eleventh of September was an amazing composite of powerful people in the Capitol. There were thirty-seven people present for the first meeting, and eleven of those were ready for the first time to admit their struggles and ask for help. The First Lady's courageous lead motivated the first of what became a ground swell in Washington to join in the fight to stem the addiction.

After much conversation with her family, Shel scheduled a complete inpatient recovery session at the Betty Ford Center. Since she planned to home-school Sheldie during the fall, the inpatient program was not scheduled until mid-November. She would be away over the Thanksgiving holidays, but home by Christmas.

She continued to attend twelve step meetings as often as her schedule permitted.

As Indian Summer approached in Washington, the President and First Lady were seen almost nightly walking arm-in-arm around the White House grounds like a couple of love-struck children. Perhaps they were.

KenField Institute

"Achievement is largely the product of steadily
raising one's levels of aspiration and expectation."

JACK NICKLAUS

Ryan got up from the couch where he had perched during the telling
of the story, walked over to the refrigerator under the counter by the
west wall of windows in my study and opened a can of orange soda. I never
understood why he liked them, but that had been his refreshment of choice
since he was just a toddler.

"Pop," he asked, "where did you come into this picture?"

"Are you *absolutely sure* you want to hear the rest of this tonight?" I
questioned. "It's getting late."

"Come on, Pop," he said. "I'm game if you are."

I sighed and said. "Many people thought the President's preoccupation with
family issues would recede after the new wore off, but Crawford was a man
of his word. After Labor Day a conference attended by the President, First Lady,
the Secretary of Health and Human Services and the *six wise men* was held
at Camp David. Purpose of the conference was to draft the preliminary plan
to change the way American society practices the art of family life.

"It was during that conference that Billy Graham told the President
about KenField Institute and your Grammy and me.

"Do you remember when you were a little tyke and we lived in Plano? You used to want to come over and play with Grammy's toys and cars all the time."

Ryan grinned and nodded.

"Well," I said, "across the street from us lived Johnson and Beth Ellis and their three kids. Landon is three or four years older than you, Sheridan is about a year younger than you and Graham, who was named for Billy Graham, is about your brother Robert's age.

"They were an ideal little family and the nicest neighbors. Beth was part of the advance team for the Billy Graham Evangelistic Team and was gone periodically to do public relations for crusades. When Grammy and I first formed KenField back in the eighties, we talked to Johnson and Beth about it often. Apparently she had shared what we were doing with someone on the Billy Graham Team and it had gotten back to Billy Graham.

"Anyway, did you ever see the Manifesto that Grammy and I wrote back then that describes what we've been doing all these years?"

He said he had not and I asked, "Well, would you like to?"

He said he would, so I said, "All right, let me find you a copy. You can read it while I take a break. As my old granddaddy used to tell me, *never pass up a drinking fountain or a bathroom and you'll live a long time.* Then I'm going to see if Grammy has any coffee on. I'll be back by the time you've read it."

I rummaged around in my desk and found a yellowed copy, which I handed him. I ruffled his hair and headed for the bathroom on my way to the kitchen.

•••

[Author's note: The KenField Manifesto is the author's journal of the birth of the dream for KenField Institute.

The Thesis for the Manifesto: Values and practices that make it possible for society to maintain social order are slowly but inexorably being eroded generation after generation. This condition continues to produce more dysfunctional families as each new generation arrives.

KenField Institute is an independently and permanently endowed private foundation for research, influence, program development and implementation designed to change for the better the way we "conduct" family life in the United States.

A copy of the full text of the Manifesto is included in the appendix.]

•••

I knew what he was reading as I poured up the last of the coffee—the notion that we are getting worse as a nation the longer we live, that to the breakdown of the family can be attributed many of the social problems we face today, that most of the solutions that have been proposed have been prescriptive rather than preventive, and that the problem is so big and so insidious as to discourage anyone who seriously wants to make a difference.

In my mind's eye I saw him awaken to the reality that unless we engage several major segments of our society at once, we may never be successful in changing the way we practice the art of family in our nation. I smiled as I could hear the gears turning as he looked at the roles and responsibilities of government, business and industry, education, religion, media and entertainment, and healthcare delivery systems in helping us create a society of effective families. There must be a coordinated effort if we have any chance of making real changes in one generation—his generation.

I saw the light dawn on him that it will be necessary for us to sanity check everything we propose and implement against the special needs of men, women, youth, children, the law, and differences in ethnic and cultural practices.

While I emptied and refilled the dishwasher and cleaned up the kitchen, I could feel the energy that caused his eyes to widen even farther when he came to the part about the staggering amount of the financial resources required to do this work.

Finally, I closed my eyes and saw him hover like the mosquito at the nudist colony—knowing what to do, just not where to start—over the enormity of the task the old Manifesto foreshadowed.

When I was sure that he was about to that point in his reading, I stopped puttering around in the kitchen and made my way back downstairs.

•••

Ryan looked up at me quizzically when I came back in the study with a fresh cup of coffee and said, "So this is what you've been doing?"

"Well, sort of," I replied, "but let me give you the *Readers Digest* condensed version. "By the time President Crawford and Billy Graham had invited us to the Camp David summit, Grammy and I had already been at work for nearly four years. We took the outline you just finished, set up our organization and built the campus where the offices are now."

"But, Pop, where did you get the money to do all that?" Ryan asked. "I mean the golf course and the office building and the ranches and all. Did the government give you the money?"

I laughed. "No, Ryan, we've never taken a dime from the government…and I don't ever expect to. We just set out with four principles in mind to characterize our work. They were, *first* of all, that KFI would seek independent and permanent private endowment so the work would last forever. *Second*, we would invest the permanent endowment in a manner that would ensure enough money each year so that we will never have to solicit contributions from our constituents. *Third*, that KFI would maintain fierce independence without any governmental strings. And, *fourth*, KFI would develop a succession plan to ensure that the original intent will continue long after Grammy and I are gone.

"Here's how it happened. Before Grammy and I married, back before you were born, I was looking for some venture capital for a project to manufacture some high-tech firearms…if you can believe that. While we were raising money for that project I met one of the most incredible men I have ever known. Someday I'll tell you about him, but not until I'm about a hundred years old. His story has been sealed until 2045, but when it does come out, you'll be alive to read about it. And, since my grand-mother lived beyond one hundred and nine, so may I.

"In the meantime," I said, "let's just call him *J. Barresford Tipton*. That was a guy who was the unseen hero of an old black and white television show about a man who sent a representative around the country giving unsuspecting people a check for one million dollars, then watching what the sudden wealth did to them. The show was called *The Millionaire*. I used to watch it when I was about ten years old, and pal, one million dollars back in the nineteen fifties was a **lot** of money.

"This wonderful man...the one I'm calling *J. Barresford Tipton*...and his wife fell in love with us and we with them. We sent them pictures of you guys while you were young. They treated us like their children...and you, your mom and dad like their own grandchildren and great-grandchildren.

"This man had amassed a massive private fortune in his lifetime of exotic careers. Some eight to ten years after we met them, we asked them to consider providing the permanent endowment we needed to do what we are doing today at KFI. They graciously agreed, and that was when we set up the charitable foundation back in ninety-nine and received their enormous gift. That ensured the first principle.

"The second principle," I said, "is one that we continue to work every year. You, of course, know our great friends Skip and Gloria Craig. Skip spent more than twenty years with Merrill Lynch before joining KFI as senior vice president and chief financial officer. It's the job of his department to ensure that our endowment funds are invested each year so that we can get a minimum five percent return annually to fund our ongoing work. Fortunately over the nearly fifteen years since we started, Skip has managed to earn slightly more than nine percent return annually...and has never lost a dollar of our endowment. We should have enough money to see that this work continues as long as our nation and its economy exists."

I paused, then said, "The third principle is really more of a decision than it is a principle. We simply do not want to be beholden to any organization that might at some point hold us hostage to any philosophy or set of rules. We take no government funds and consequently are in position to criticize or praise governmental stances on family issues.

"The fourth principle is meant to ensure that the work of KenField Institute continues uninterrupted forever. We enlist men and women for key positions a minimum of ten to fifteen years prior to the time we expect them to assume the reins of authority. That is why your dad works with Skip in managing the endowment funds. When Skip retires in a couple of years, your father will have worked with him for nearly fifteen years. He will be ready to assume complete responsibility for our investments by then.

"Then, over the next ten years or so, he will be looking for someone to understudy him. And so it goes on. We want the understudies not only to learn the skills required, but to gain the heart and sense of urgency that characterizes what drove Grammy and me into this work. Our executive committee and the key members of our staff all work under this principle.

"So there you have it. We have been making come true the dream you just read about."

The Beginning

It was late. Ryan and I had sat in my study and talked until well after two in the morning.

"Are you game to hear this for about thirty more minutes," I asked, "or have you had enough?"

He laughed. "Are you kidding? There's no way I could sleep now...not without hearing what happened after President Crawford invited you to Camp David?"

I had to get up and move a little. My old bones were getting tired of sitting. I paced about the room a bit and recalled the early days in nineteen ninety-nine before we knew there was going to be a President Crawford. That year we started receiving the endowment and operating funds.

We also gathered the families that had dreamed this dream with us for more than fifteen years and celebrated the launching of our very own *Field of Dreams*. They were: Stan and Gloria Craig; David and Nancy Humphrey; Barry and Dena Brelsford; Paul and Marilyn Royal; Doug and Marah Dillard; and the twenty-three children and twenty-five grandchildren we all represented. It was a memorable celebration of thanksgiving for the privilege of carrying the banner for healthy families into the twenty-first century.

It was in nineteen ninety-nine that we planned our immediate course of action and enlisted our staff. We set up temporary offices in the Galleria Towers in Dallas. We enlisted the help of Cecil Pearson, retired chief executive officer of the California Baptist Foundation, to assist us in the establishment of the KenField Institute Foundation and Trusts and to help us secure the proper status from IRS. He worked with Stan Craig in developing the strategies for investment of the endowment funds to maximize return and insure safety of the principal.

In addition we began negotiations with ClubCorp of America for acquisition of the country club that is now the site of our headquarters facility. And, by year's end we had bought the Oak Lake Ranch site, the home of Koinonia Lodge, the Millhurst Farms ranch, the headquarters site in Dallas and had begun construction on The Center at Millhurst and the HQ facility.

We opened our first satellite lobbying office in Washington, D.C.

By the end of nineteen ninety-nine we had all our staff in place—one hundred fifty-eight in all. The Center (a residential facility for the promotion of healthy families and recovery from dysfunction) had been completed at Millhurst Farms and the first pilot projects were being conducted there with some of our own families as the early participants. Koinonia Lodge (a family-centric retreat facility offering family conferences, seminars and counseling) was filled nearly every week as people from all over the nation came to renew their commitments to their families and to celebrate their skills as husbands and fathers and wives and mothers. We were fortunate enough to attract some of the world's foremost authorities on family life to direct weekend workshops at Koinonia—John Gray, John Bradshaw, Gary Smalley, Harville Hendrix, Pia Mellody, James Dobson, Chuck Swindoll, Paul Faulkner and even the members of our own executive staff. There was always a waiting list.

We had enlisted some outstanding people to serve on our advisory boards and to serve as spokespersons for key family issues:

- *Government*—Dan Quayle, Jimmy Carter, George W. Bush, John Ashcroft, Colin Powell and Rockland and Shelby Crawford.
- *Business and Industry*—William Gates, Ross Perot, Herb Kelleher and Roger Staubach.
- *Education*—William Mitchell, Steven Covey and LeAnn Linden.
- *Media & Entertainment*—Bill Cosby, Ron Howard, Reggie White, Ted Baehr and Mel Gibson.
- *Religion*—Chuck Swindoll, James Dobson, Jesse Jackson, Frank Pollard and Paul Powell.
- *Healthcare Delivery Systems*—Edward Koop, Red Duke, Laura Schlesinger, John Bradshaw, Gary Smalley, Pia Mellody, Pat Love, Harville Hendrix, William Parisi and Carolyn Galloway.

We had also built one of the most sophisticated processing centers for information in existence at that time. We used it to gather and disseminate knowledge on healthy family practices through a variety of media across the nation. We had up-link capabilities through the Dallas/Fort Worth Teleport satellites and could broadcast and multicast over our multiple forty-five million bps links to the Internet from our production studios anywhere in the world.

We had created a database and clearinghouse for every program and agency we could find who was offering curriculum, programming help, advice, education or services in behalf of "the family." As we approached the new millennium, we had more than eleven thousand two hundred and fifty listings in our database with website links to many of them. Our website averaged more than fifty-seven thousand hits a month during the first two years of operation and has been growing ever since.

We had initiatives in each directorate for program rollouts scheduled for the first decade of the new century.

In the year two thousand we developed a pilot project with Chrysler Corporation to include basic family skills training in the company's regular employee training. We tracked that program for five years and quantified the differences in absenteeism, quality of production output, divorces, terminations which came within six months—either way—of divorce. We compared the five years immediately prior to the pilot project to the years of the project. Chrysler experienced a three-percent improvement in defect reduction in their production and reduced involuntary termination rates for the same period by more than eleven-percent. Employee surveys of perceived satisfaction with their employment at Chrysler improved by seventeen and a half percent during the evaluation period.

The J.C. Penney Corporation headquarters facility had similar programs that they agreed to expand as a result of Chrysler's results. Penney already had onsite childcare, fitness center, healthcare facility and flex scheduling as part of their employee benefit package.

During the year two thousand we launched the KenField Awards. Our long-term goal was to make this as prestigious an award as the Nobel or Pulitzer prizes each year. We had budgeted enough endowment to provide distribution of six million dollars annually to be awarded in one million-dollar increment to the individuals, organizations or agencies that had made the most significant contribution to the improvement of *the family* during the previous twelve months.

That first year we only made two awards. The celebration was at the Infomart in Dallas with more than one thousand people in attendance. Recipients were James Dobson of *Focus on the Family* and WFAA Television, Dallax TX for its local *Family First* emphases.

"Hello, Pop, remember me?" Ryan asked. "Where did you go?"

I had, obviously, been lost in thought. "Sorry, pal, just remembering lots of pleasant memories that led up to our invitation to Camp David.

"We kept our home in Plano, Texas when we moved out here to the country in the winter of nineteen ninety-nine. Do you remember helping us move when you were about five or six?"

He grinned and nodded.

"Since we worked in Dallas," I said, "we needed a home there when we were in town for several days at a time.

"You remember me reminding you about Johnson and Beth Ellis...Landon, Sheridan and Graham's mom and dad? Well, we were helping her host our annual *block party* over the Labor Day weekend in two thousand two when she mentioned to Grammy and me that she had told Billy Graham about what we were doing at KFI. I thought that was nice, but dismissed the thought almost as quickly as it arrived. So, it was a real shock when Florence James called the office that next week with an invitation to meet President Crawford at Camp David on the last weekend in September. When I asked her how and why, she told us about the recommendation from Billy Graham.

"Grammy couldn't wait to tell Beth. But, we blew it off and told Beth we couldn't go."

"You're kidding," Ryan said. "You didn't go? You turned down the President?"

I laughed. "No, kid, I'm pulling your leg. Grammy, Stan and Gloria Craig and I flew into Dulles Airport on that Friday morning and were met by a government car and driver. By noon we were at Camp David.

"Over the next three days we met the President and Mrs. Crawford, Barry Roberts and Coach McCartney. Bill Cosby joined us by video conference on Saturday afternoon. We spoke to Billy Graham on the phone. We would meet him later...and often.

"We had sent the President a copy of our Manifesto and a scrapbook of what we had accomplished over the previous four years. The more he heard the more excited he and Shel became. We were doing what they had made commitments to do in the last days of their first term.

"Ryan, the President of the United States invited us to tell him what we could do together to make the world a better place for his new granddaughter. He said that anything we needed from him we could have.

"We talked a long time about the initiatives our Government

Directive had developed over those years. One of those initiatives was a permanent Presidential Commission focusing on the issues affecting American Families.

"Another was a tax incentive for well functioning families. This would include tax breaks for new families that do certain preparation activities prior to marriage...a twenty-five percent annual federal income tax deduction for people married for twenty-five years to the same person...and a fifty percent lifetime tax break for people celebrating their golden wedding anniversary.

"Another initiative we discussed was serious welfare reform to encourage families who do what is right...and to not reward families formed and operated irresponsibly. This included identification and accountability of the father of every child born.

"We discussed educational tax incentives for families participating in training sessions designed to foster better families and a tax incentive for corporations that offer affirmative family plans as part of their benefits and training packages.

"It was a terrific weekend...and it would not be the last we experienced during the remainder of the Crawford White House years. Both Rocko and Shel are now on our advisory board.

"You will," I said, "recall from history class that President Crawford's forthrightness in his *Roshelle* speech when she first came home to the White House made him even more the darling of the American public. He was re-elected for a second term. The candor of that speech and his willingness to cast his Presidential future on the mercies of the people endeared him to the voting public not unlike what happened when Abraham Lincoln delivered the *Gettysburg Address* and Richard Nixon delivered his *Checkers* speech many years ago. Apparently we still like an honest man...warts and all.

"We left Camp David that weekend with a clear assurance that we had a very powerful ally in the White House. What happened thereafter would prove that to be true.

"Let me just give you a scrapbook's-eye view of what we have accomplished since that time, much of it as a result of the unabashed support of Rocko and Shel Crawford.

"Today, we have the tax breaks I mentioned to you earlier. We offer families the opportunity to use up to fifteen hundred dollars of their annual federal tax liabilities to fund *how-to* family training at community colleges, churches and private companies all across the country.

"The President's Commission on Families is a permanent watchdog organization upon whom we rely very heavily for government involvement. We assist them every year by providing a sixty-minute video to each member of Congress that highlights key issues affecting families. We offer recommendations to the Administration and to the Congress on legislation and executive orders that we believe will make a difference that year. The content of this video sets the tone for the strong lobbying efforts that we make at the federal and State levels. We have lobbyists at work in every state capitol and in Washington, D.C.

"Many of the original recommendations of President George Bush's Commission on Urban Families have been implemented. Do you remember reading them in the Manifesto I gave you earlier this evening?"

Ryan nodded in the affirmative, but seemed too intent on listening to say anything—so I continued.

"We also launched a massive campaign to turn the American public back to a net investing nation," I said. "The shift from consumption to investment simply means that each of us has to consume at a slower rate than the growth of the GNP…or gross national product. It's our contention that failure to do this now will have devastating impact on our families in another generation. This suggests some small burdens in your generation, pal, but if we fail to do this it will impose major burdens on your children. This is one of those ongoing areas where our biggest problem is not solving the problem, but getting our stubborn nation to recognize that we have a problem. In two thousand and one, for the first time in nearly a century, we reduced consumption below the level of growth of the GNP.

"The system of education in the United States has undergone several major overhauls. We've moved toward schedules of two hundred twenty days a year. We're on a track to raise the pay for teachers to a level commensurate with industrial salaries. We've spawned an aggressive effort at skills-set education that is specific to business and industry. We've enhanced the math and science requirements for college bound students. We've worked with the major universities in twenty-two states to develop industry specific skill sets and train graduates to fill them in high tech, petrochemical, telecommunications, information systems and technology, aerospace and electronic commerce. We've developed a new generation of quality standard achievement tests for college entrance, assuring that high school graduates have the necessary skills to work at America's best firms.

"Seventy of the top one hundred municipalities or counties in the country have adopted a requirement that marriage licenses must be preceded by a Plato-system (touch screen response computer based) inventory that is a derivative of the *Prepare/Enrich* inventory of Life Innovations, Inc. Couples take the inventory while waiting to receive their marriage licenses and are given a printout highlighting their strengths and growth areas in relationship. Each applicant for a marriage license also receives a handbook/workbook and video as a follow on to their Plato inventory. The packet includes recommended local training resources and a national interactive video/audio hotline available over the Internet to assist in dealing with growth issues.

"We've established corporate *family friendly training* programs in one hundred twenty-six of the Fortune Five Hundred companies, and have one hundred eighty-seven more under negotiation.

"We have established a media consortium in which many of the most influential members have been enlisted to participate. Bill Cosby, Ted Baehr and Coach McCartney were instrumental in enlisting representatives from the movies, television, professional sports, all forms of music, print media, radio and the theater. The consortium has created a standard of excellence in which they vigorously encourage others in their fields to adopt standards of content and conduct that uphold high values. A growing number of media purveyors carry the *KenField Seal of Approval* for their movies, television programs, advertisements, music lyrics and videos. It's not enough, but it is a start.

"More than five hundred national advertisers and twenty-seven million families have subscribed to the high standards of the *KenField Seal of Approval* in support of advertisers and entertainers who demonstrate 'family friendly' content and style.

"More than eleven hundred and fifty school districts in the country have adopted our Practical Life-Curriculum and have enlisted local community support to teach the course to junior/senior high school students. All the *how to* things you read about earlier in the Manifesto are included in the curriculum outline.

"You took our course in high school, didn't you, Ryan?"

He smiled that easy smile again. "Yeah, Pop, and my dad volunteered as one of my teachers. Don't you remember?"

I did remember—and was proud of our son for volunteering. The program we designed calls for community leaders to volunteer to learn the family-friendly *how to* curriculum and teach one or two sections per week in a middle or high school. Ryan's dad, Rick, had been one of our first volunteers.

"The KenField Awards are now as big as any award program in the country," I told Ryan. "It's held annually in Washington, D.C. at the John F. Kennedy Center for the Performing Arts in the first week of June. This year we played to a packed house when we made the awards to the six one million dollar winners.

"Seventeen major Protestant denominations, the Roman Catholic Church, American Jewry and the Greek Orthodox Church have all subscribed to the broad standards of testing, marriage preparation, a program of follow up and mentoring for newly married people, marriage enrichment programs and accountability. *Promise Keepers* has grown to have more than twenty million men who have participated in their local events.

"We have launched a program to offer stipends to young seminary families who will soon lead our nation's religious communities. The seminarians spend one weekend per month at Koinonia Lodge for intensive training in family values and skills. In exchange, we give these struggling families up to one thousand dollars per month in extra income while they are in school. In exchange, these young families are committed to helping us enlist a half million families that will become neighborhood captains carrying the message of strong families to their neighbors over the next twenty years. Today our seminary graduates have already been instrumental in enlisting nearly one hundred thousand of these neighborhood captains to help us. By two thousand and twenty we expect to reach our goal.

"Finally, we have made real progress in the delivery of good mental health services for family issues, ranging from couple relationships to parenting issues. Bill Gates has placed the not inconsiderable resources of the Microsoft Corporation behind the development of an Internet search engine that has enabled us to produce and provide interactive on-line services dealing with virtually every topic imaginable that affects family life. Edward Koop, former Surgeon General of the United States has even created a permanently staffed hotline service to augment the interactive on-line service. We are still committed to the premise that a combination of Internet/interactive/virtual reality services, neighborhood mentoring programs, small group development and self help programs will help us deliver the required support that families need regardless of their ability to pay.

"As you can see we've come a long way, but there's still lots of work to do. Unfortunately we'll never get it all done. Even if we develop every conceivable program and implement every conceivable action, we'll have to begin again new each generation to attack the enemies of the family and to enlist new warriors in the fight to preserve and defend it.

"Each generation will have to renew this challenge as long as our nation lasts. No matter how well we have performed for this generation, we'll have to begin again with yours.

"So, Ryan, are you still game to be part of this grand adventure?"

Boiling the Frog

"To achieve the marvelous, it is precisely the unthinkable that must be thought."
TOM ROBBINS.

The world has had its share of stupid statements—shortsighted statements, or maybe just statements that have since been proved to lack the kind of vision required for change. They serve as everlasting monuments to the relative stupidity of mankind in general and the ease with which we can be sold a bill of goods.

"I think there is a world market for maybe five computers."
THOMAS WATSON, CHAIRMAN OF IBM, 1943.

"I have traveled the length and breadth of this country and talked with the best people, and I can assure you that data processing is a fad that won't last out the year."
THE EDITOR IN CHARGE OF BUSINESS BOOKS FOR PRENTICE HALL, 1957.

"A cookie store is a bad idea. Besides, the market research reports say America likes crispy cookies, not soft and chewy cookies like you make."
RESPONSE TO DEBBI FIELDS' IDEA FOR STARTING MRS. FIELDS COOKIES.

"We don't like their sound, and guitar music is on the way out."
DECCA RECORDING COMPANY, REJECTING THE BEATLES, 1962.

"Heavier than air flying machines are impossible."

LORD KELVIN, PRESIDENT, ROYAL SOCIETY, 1895.

"So we went to Atari and said, 'Hey, we've got this amazing thing, even built with some of your parts, and what do you think about funding us? Or, we'll give it to you. We just want to do it. Pay our salary, we'll come work for you.' And they said, 'No.' So then we went to Hewlett-Packard, and they said, 'Hey we don't need you. You haven't got through college yet.'"

APPLE COMPUTER INC. FOUNDER STEVE JOBS ON ATTEMPTS TO GET ATARI AND H-P INTERESTED IN HIS AND STEVE WOZNIAK'S PERSONAL COMPUTER.

"Drill for oil? You mean drill into the ground to try and find oil? You're crazy."

DRILLERS EDWIN L. DRAKE TRIED TO ENLIST TO HIS PROJECT TO DRILL FOR OIL IN 1859.

"Stocks have reached what looks like a permanently high plateau."

IRVING FISHER, PROFESSOR OF ECONOMICS, YALE UNIVERSITY, 1929.

"Everything that can be invented has been invented."

CHARLES H. DUELL, COMMISSIONER, U.S. OFFICE OF PATENTS, 1899.

"640K ought to be enough for anybody."

BILL GATES, 1981

We have been told for years that it is not possible to turn the practices of family life in this nation around within a generation. Someone once likened my passion for families to that of Noah who built a massive boat on dry land, far from any known water in a land where it had never rained before.

Actually, the comparison was made to my bride as Mrs. Noah. How do you think she felt? What did her neighbors say? Did she ever think her husband was nuts? How do you suppose they were treated? How much opposition did they attract? Was it ever lonely in their quest? Did their friends ever question their sanity?

The truth is that individual passion and commitment can still make impossible things happen. That is and has been the work of KenField Institute.

Just for fun, let's do a quick review of the progressive evolution of family life in the twentieth century.

This could be a statistically supported report, but I want you to use your perception, intuition and knowledge to verify the truth of the informal history of *family* in our society.

THE AGRARIAN FAMILY

Back in the eighteenth century, when most Americans lived on small self-sufficient farms, each family produced most of what it consumed—food, clothing, candles, fuel, furniture. Anything that was surplus was sold for the things they could not produce.

Extended family units, or clans, lived in proximity and frequently worked together to produce enough to live.

Families were typically stable, regardless of their functionality. One man, one woman, together for life. Large numbers of children were not uncommon. Birth control, other than abstinence, was not available. Children were viewed as more hands to work in the harvests. Even our nine-month school term system was devised around harvest time so that children would be free to help in the summer harvests.

Children married early, frequently in their teenage years. Divorce was basically unheard of and sex outside marriage was generally confined to bordellos and then not countenanced by polite society.

Neighborliness was the order of the day.

THE INDUSTRIAL REVOLUTION

Change began to occur with the advent of the Industrial Revolution. English and American inventiveness gave us the flying shuttle (eighteenth century English inventor John Kay), the spinning jenny (eighteenth century English inventor James Hargreaves), the steam engine (eighteenth century English inventor James Watts) and the cotton gin (nineteen century American inventor Eli Whitney).

These and associated inventions put farmers in factories. Dad left the farm home each day for a job in the factory. Jobs were generally less rewarding than farming had been and assembly line positions replaced a form of labor that had allowed a farm family to see a finished product, rather than merely work on one stage of its production.

Henry Ford's assembly line placed the manager bosses above the line. They could see the end from the beginning and understood the processes. The laborers on the line were generally unlearned farmers who were not trusted by the manager bosses to be part of the process. Sufficient for them to make sure the right number of nuts were screwed to the right number of bolts every day. The end result for the laborer was monotony, boredom, loss of joy in work and loss of self-worth for having had to trade their outdoor creative farming lives for indoor plumbing and twenty-five cents an hour in order to provide for their families.

Railroads, improved iron manufacture, sky scraper construction and the automobile forever changed the natural pattern of family continuity. Dad was away from home all day. More items were bought rather than produced. Fewer children were required in order to maintain the family's livelihood.

The Industrial Revolution spanned a period from seventeen hundred to the end of World War II.

Henry David Thoreau asked where all this progress was leading. From the shores of Walden Pond, he surveyed the world of the mid nineteenth century and asked whether all of this *progress* was not merely "an improved means to an unimproved end." Even he, though, admitted that there was something exciting about the trains that he heard passing his cabin.

As the extended family eroded in the face of the Industrial Revolution, so the number of children born began to decline. From the early days of the nineteenth century when the average number of children was seven per family, the late twentieth century saw that number fall to two or less per family. At the same time people began marrying later and living longer lives. And, since the age of the parents was younger at the birth of the last child, many husbands and wives had about as many years together after their children left home as they had during child rearing years.

POST WORLD WAR II FAMILIES

Are we boiling the frog yet?

In the name of tolerance, sophistication and progress, we have gradually eroded some awfully basic principles. Take a quick and cursory look at the influences that have changed the American family since the nineteen forties.

- ■ Free and easy credit is a major problem. Until the late nineteen forties there was no such thing as consumer credit. Today you cannot sit down to a meal in the evening in your home without having to encounter multiple *credit card deals* from telemarketers. We have moved from being a net saver nation to a net debtor nation, corporately and personally. Perhaps one of the most insidious burdens on the successful practice of family life has been the impact of negative compound interest on credit cards. For example, a pizza costing twelve dollars purchased on a major credit card and paid for with only the minimum payment each month will take thirty-three years to repay and ultimately cost ninety-one dollars. Has anyone ever had a pizza worth ninety-one dollars?

- ■ In nineteen ninety-one, for the first time in more than a hundred years, America became a net payer rather than a net receiver of foreign-investment income. Sooner or later the lending will stop and real interest rates will explode. Then the foreign investment will stop altogether.

- ■ We have embraced a growing admiration of the ideology of individualism versus the ideology of a strong family.

- ■ The rise of a strong middle class has led to the virtual elimination of arranged marriages and tolerance for romantic marriages of free choice.

- ■ An explosion of premarital sex has occurred as sexual taboos have been relaxed and the age of marrying has increased from late teens to early twenties after World War II. Today it is not uncommon

167

to see marriages postponed until late twenties, thirties or beyond.

■ There is increased tolerance for *dirty* language, overt sex, nudity, violence, drug abuse and alcohol abuse in movies, television, music and print. It is a long way from the shock and outrage of the late nineteen thirties when Clark Gable said, "Frankly, my dear, I don't give a damn."

■ The women's movement and a dramatic increase of women pursuing careers outside of homemaking have taken its toll on families.

■ There have been dramatic changes in the independent economic status of women.

■ Divorce laws have been liberalized.

■ The legal grounds for divorce have been reduced.

■ There has been a removal of the social stigma related to divorce.

■ According to a report in the *Congressional Quarterly* citing William Bennett's book, *Index of Leading Cultural Indicators*, problems in public school have changed since the nineteen forties when the major concerns of teachers were talking out of turn, gum chewing, making noise, running the halls, cutting in line, inappropriate dress and littering. Problems that concern teachers today are drug abuse, alcohol abuse, pregnancy, suicide, rape, robbery and assault.

■ The legalization of abortion has practically destroyed accountability.

■ There has been a dramatic increase in the number of teenage unwed pregnancies—children trading Barbie for babies.

■ There has been exponential growth in teenage suicide, illegitimate births and divorce rates—and the incidence of single parent homes has outpaced the population growth by hundreds of percentage points.

■ Women now have more to fear from domestic violence than any other health hazard they face today, including breast cancer. Husbands and boy friends beat more than four million women each year.

■ Schools report a dramatic drop in scholastic aptitude testing by more than seventy points.

■ More than twenty-five percent of all high school students have contracted a sexually transmitted disease before they graduate from high school.

■ Improved and accessible contraceptives have made sex more attractive to children.

■ The stigma associated with children being born out of wedlock has been removed.

■ There has been acceptance of Common Law marriages.

■ We continue to live with antiquated laws requiring elderly unmarried people to live together without benefit of marriage in order to retain their social security benefits.

■ Other institutions now perform certain functions previously reserved for family—education, economic production, religion and recreation.

■ Mass media and peers have at least as much influence on the socialization of children as the family.

■ Extended family households have declined dramatically.

■ Residential and employment mobility have fragmented families.

■ Pension and investment funds have reduced the responsibility of children for aging parents.

■ Alternate 'family styles' are finding more acceptances—persons of opposite sex sharing living quarters (POSSLQ), homosexual couples, communal family and common law marriage.

Carle Zimmerman in *Family and Civilization* wrote in nineteen forty-seven comparing the dissolution of numerous historical cultures with the decline of the family unit in America. Remember that what you are about to read was written in nineteen forty-seven. Imagine the spin he might put on this information more than a half century later. He identified specific behavioral patterns that typified the final stages of each culture he studied. Just prior to their end, certain conditions were uniformly observed. The observations speak for themselves:

■ Increased and rapid, easy, 'causeless' divorce.

■ Decreased number of children, population decay and increased pub-

lic disrespect for parents and parenthood.
- ■ Elimination of the real meaning of the marriage ceremony.
- ■ Popularity of pessimistic doctrines about the early heroes.
- ■ Breaking down of most inhibitions against adultery.
- ■ Revolts of youth against parents so that parenthood became more and more difficult for those who did try to raise children.
- ■ Rapid rise and spread of juvenile delinquency.
- ■ Common acceptance of all forms of sex perversions.

But just for a moment take a simpler view. Can you remember when you could traverse the country *on your thumb?* Within my lifetime, college students and young men in military service hitchhiked cross-country with ease and impunity. Today it is considered far too dangerous to offer someone a lift.

Are we boiling the frog yet?

Do you remember when a trip to town ended at a parking meter on Main Street? Nobody locked a car, and you likely left a nickel on the dashboard just in case the meter expired before you returned. You knew that the traffic officer on the beat would look on your dash and deposit your nickel if needed. Today we lock our cars, install alarms, wire in GPS tracking systems and lock the steering with *The Club.*

Are we boiling the frog yet?

There was a day when no one locked their homes, secure in the notion that we were a nation of honest folks. We watched out for each other and some of us didn't even have a key. Today, we look for the deepest double key deadbolts money can buy. We extend screw lengths into doorjambs to prevent easy entry. We build with metal clad doors. We install sophisticated alarm and monitoring systems. We buy big dogs and leave them inside all day. We purchase and practice the use of firearms for self-defense. Few of us know our neighbors by name and, heaven forbids that we might lend them a hand. We don't 'neighbor' much any more.

Are we boiling the frog yet?

Once upon a time, families sat down to mealtime together. They talked, played games and learned how to work together—even if just in the mundane things of maintaining a home. Today we thaw, microwave, eat on the run, never have sit-down meals together, glue ourselves in front of the one eyed television monster and lose ourselves in mindless entertainment to the detriment of family development and influence. Family has become a loose institution where people get their clothes laundered, eat quick meals on the run, sleep and get mail.

My objection to television is not merely that the quality of programs is depressingly low; it is also that the screen exercises a hypnotic effect on the majority of watchers... It is a terrible slavery of the mind—and as Aristotle warned us a long time ago, 'the worst thing about slavery is that eventually the slaves get to like it.'—Sidney J. Harris

Are we boiling the frog yet?

There was a day when we drove down the roads of this country and waved and nodded at our fellow drivers. In some parts of the country, it was as common to lift a hand in salute when driving along highways as it was to greet one another on the street. Today that salute is more likely to be a middle finger and, in the worst instances, someone may get shot because of road rage.

Have we boiled the frog yet?

We have taken the concept of the rights of the individual to the theater of the absurd. We convict criminals of capital crimes and then take forever to carry out the sentences. We have a prison population that is growing faster than the population of the country. We treat the prisoners better than we treat many of the poor and homeless in this country. The lowering age of criminal offenders, the leniency of the court system, the revolving doors of overcrowded systems, early release programs, and the monumental costs in excess of thirty thousand dollars per year per inmate to maintain the prison population add to the madness.

What are we really doing to go up stream to the place where the social ills are creating the climate of crime and criminals? Why are we not doing

171

the preventive things that will stop and reverse the trends?

One of our nation's most renowned profilers or *mind-hunters* is John Douglas, who for twenty-five years was Chief of the Investigative Support Unit—the operational arm of the FBI's National Center for the Analysis of Violent Crime in Quantico, Virginia. He brought the concept of profiling behavior into the criminal investigative process. His specialty was profiling serial killers.

In his incredibly stark and compelling book, *Journey into Darkness*, Douglas spoke about the ultimate solution to the slide into darkness that has created the burgeoning prison system whose sides cannot keep up with the demand for their services. He wrote:

"Ultimately, no matter what we do with our criminal justice system, the only thing that is going to cut down appreciably on crimes of violence and depravity is to stop manufacturing as many criminals. The courts have a role in this, the police have a role in this, the schools have a role, and so do the churches and synagogues and mosques. But the real struggle must be where it has always been: in the home.

"As (serial killer) Sedley Alley's prosecutor, Hank Williams, observes, 'The federal government spends billions of dollars to fight crime, and they have to. But the only real answer is for mommas and daddies to raise their kids right.

"This is easier said than done, but it's the only factor that's going to make a real difference." *(Reprinted with the permission of Scribner, a Division of Simon & Schuster from JOURNEY INTO DARKNESS by John Douglas and Mark Olshaker. Copyright (c) 1997 by Mindhunters, Inc.)*

That *is* the mission of KenField Institute. It is a guerrilla force set down in the middle of alien territory. It is possible to turn things around. We can see that our children and grandchildren live in a world populated by mothers and fathers who know how to raise their children right.

•••

One final word on frogs and families. A cursory review of Internet data and responsible print media reveals some strikingly interesting facts about frogs.

Fire up your internet browser and find http://frog.simplenet.com/frog-gy/sciam/frogs-disappear.txt and http://www.npwrc.usgs.gov/narcam/ index.html

You will read about the shocking worldwide decline in frog populations. Some species may be gone entirely, and no one can agree on the causes.

If that was not enough read in *Newsweek*, July 13, 1998, "Bad Days on the Lily Pad" by Sharon Begley. She tells of the mass deformities that are becoming more the rule than the exception in whole populations of frogs—missing legs, extra legs, missing eyes, missing jaws and more. These abnormalities are becoming more frequent, more varied and more severe each year.

How much of a stretch is it to maintain our frog/family analogy? Begley quoted USGS zoologist Kenneth Dodd about the seriousness of the problem. "This is a very serious problem. The public would be deluding itself to think it isn't. I only hope that we are not seeing the first signs of the unraveling of the biosphere."

Begley concludes, "That *ribbitt ribbitt*, in other words, may be a warning cry."

What sort of warning sound does the family in crisis make? And, who's listening?

•••

IT MUST HAVE BEEN THE GUNS

Paul Harvey read this, Letter to the Editor, on his newscast the other day in response to the massacre at Columbine High School in Littleton, Colorado. It came from the San Angelo Standard Times, 4/27/99.

"How can we blame it all on guns?"
Editor:
For the life of me, I can't understand what could have gone wrong in Littleton, Colo. If only the parents had kept their children away from the guns, we wouldn't have had such a tragedy. Yeah, it must have been the guns.

It couldn't have been because half our children are being raised in broken homes.

It couldn't have been because our children get to spend an average of 30 seconds in meaningful conversation with their parents each day. After all, we give our children quality time.

It couldn't have been because we treat our children as pets and our pets as children.

It couldn't have been because we place our children in day care centers where they learn their socialization skills among their peers under the law of the jungle while employees who have no vested interest in the children look on and make sure that no blood is spilled.

It couldn't have been because we allow our children to watch, on average, seven hours of television a day filled with the glorification of sex and violence that isn't fit for adult consumption.

It couldn't have been because we allow our children to enter into virtual worlds in which, to win the game, one must kill as many opponents as possible in the most sadistic way possible.

It couldn't have been because we have sterilized and contracepted our families down to sizes so small that the children we do have are so spoiled with material things that they come to equate the receiving of the material with love.

It couldn't have been because our children, who historically have been seen as a blessing from God, are now being viewed as either a mistake created when contraception fails or inconveniences that parents try to raise in their spare time.

It couldn't have been because our nation is the world leader in developing a culture of death in which 20 million to 30 million babies have been killed by abortion.

It couldn't have been because we give two-year prison sentences to teen-agers who kill their newborns.

It couldn't have been because our school systems teach the children that they are nothing but glorified apes who have evolutionized out of some primordial soup of mud by teaching evolution as fact and by handing out condoms as if they were candy.

It couldn't have been because we teach our children that there are no laws of morality that transcend us, that everything is relative and that actions don't have consequences. What the heck, the president gets away with it.

Nah, it must have been the guns.

Thank you, Addison L. Dawson of San Angelo, Texas. Well said, sir.

•••

There are lots of wonderful tools available today to help families turn it around in one generation. What is lacking is a national commitment to focus all the major institutions of our society on the solutions that are readily available. We are literally dying of thirst on the bank of the oasis. Let this be the generation that gets the wake up call.

•

The Rest of the Story

"...and now you know the rest of the story."

PAUL HARVEY

Ryan and I had managed to talk the night away. I can't believe we sat up all night. I haven't done that in more years than I care to remember. It's a good thing that I don't need more than three to four hours sleep.

After we had talked about the accomplishments that KFI has achieved, we began to talk earnestly about where he might fit into our family next summer. Just as the sun was coming up...

"Pop, I don't really know where I'd like to work. Is there any possibility that I might get some project assignments and work in several departments or whatever you call them?

"That's probably not a bad idea, Squirt. There is no magic in names, but we call our departments "directorates" or "support services." I think we could get you some project work in operations with Barry Brelsford or out here at the Center with Paul. As I think about it, though, those assignments would be more facilities and maintenance or security projects and you may be more interested in substantive core products. Umm..."

He gave me that intense look again. "Pop, you know I always like coming out here to the ranch and working around the Center, but I'd like to find something that might become a permanent assignment when I get out of school. Do you do any research on the internet? Do you need any website work? or proposal writing? I'd even be willing to work with my Dad in the investments section."

"Well, you can't work for your Dad. The one thing we have insisted upon is that we don't let family members report to family members. I'm not sure that you have enough background to work in the portfolio management section, but I bet we can find you something working with one of the Directorates—like maybe the Education folks. That is something you are certainly close to.

"On the other hand, you might like to work with David Dillard. He has been my understudy for more than fifteen years now and will be taking my place in the next few years. That way you could see how the whole organization works, and he could assign you on the projects that need the most help during the summers."

We have known David and Karen Dillard for a long time. His old daddy and I have been colleagues for more than fifty years. I've known David since he was a little boy. They have one lovely daughter, Caroline. She's grown up to be a very pretty young lady like her mother., and even though she is two years older than Ryan, they have grown up around each other. David was and is and has always been my choice to succeed me as CEO of KFI. He has been with us since early 1999. I do not know how we could have accomplished all we have without his steady hand and time-ly counsel.

I could tell that Ryan was turning that concept over in his mind. When he finally responded, he surprised me again. "Pop, I know that my Dad and David have worked for you all a long time. It's like a second string or junior varsity thing, right?"

I stopped him in the middle of that thought. "No, pal, there is noth-ing second string about either of these guys. You recall the fourth oper-ating principle we talked about last night? Our plan is to enlist men and women for key positions a minimum of ten to fifteen years prior to the time we expect them to assume control. That is why your Dad has worked for Skip for fifteen years in managing our portfolios. When Skip retires and I retire, your Dad and David will take our places. The key thing for Grammy and me is that we have people to whom to hand our vision who have the same sense of urgency that we do. Your Dad and David have demonstrated that kind of stuff for years."

He was silent for a long time. Finally, he asked softly, "Pop, if this intern thing works out for both of us, what are the chances that I could become one of those understudies?"

Brought a tear to my eye. My turn to be quiet. I hope there will always be one of our offspring at KFI. I whispered a silent prayer that this germ of passion for our dream might take shape and grow in this fine young man.

"If you still feel that way after you finish your undergraduate work, and I'm still alive by then, come ask me that question again. There is nothing that would please me more. Now go wash your face and comb your hair and let's pretend we're just getting up for breakfast. If we're lucky everybody will just think we got up early."

Call to Action

Maybe KenField is or will be a reality. Maybe not. Maybe J. Barresford Tipton is alive and well or maybe he's just part of the author's fertile imagination. Maybe some of you who read this book are J. Barresford Tiptons and will read and be motivated to underwrite this effort. Either way, the call to action by everyone who gets this wake-up call is imperative.

Let us hear from you at *www.kenfieldinstitute.com*, or write to KenField Institute, PO Box 704011, Dallas, TX 75370.

YOU need to take action TODAY. There is something to do for everyone who reads and hears this story.

1. Begin by examining the emotional health of your own family relationships—your spouse, children, parents, grandparents, grandchildren. Is there a firm resolve to create healthy family systems in your home? How are you going about that today? What's working well? What isn't? Do you need a recommitment to the vows of your marriage? Are you getting any help? Where? Do you know where to begin? Start today to find out where the resources are and do what it takes to create a healthy family in YOUR home. Go to your neighborhood bookstore and browse.

Go online and search the internet. Inquire at your local community college. Find out what your church offers. It will require conscious and deliberate changes in behaviors.

2. Review the action items included in the KenField Manifesto in the appendix. Call and write your government representatives—local, state and federal. If you don't know who your representatives are, call your local city hall. Someone can give you contact information. Encourage them regularly to enact legislation that is family friendly. Make your voice heard. Ask your neighbors to join you. Engage the parents of your children's friends in the lobbying efforts. Call for change. Don't take NO for an answer.

3. Visit your children's school leadership—classroom teachers, principals, superintendent, state agency. Ask them about the practical life-curriculum issues that the KenField Manifesto raises. Are they being taught? By whom? At what grade levels? If not, why not? Volunteer. Gather community resources to develop curriculum materials that can be taught by career teachers or by community volunteers. Volunteer. Just get started.

4. Ask your employer what is being done proactively to support and encourage healthy family relationships among employees and staff. Recommend the inclusion of marriage and family enrichment training as part of the regular training that supports the business. Keep the dialogue alive and don't take NO for an answer. Ask again.

5. Find out what your church is doing to support marriage preparation and marriage enrichment. If your church does not have a marriage preparation seminar that meets weekly for a period of three to four months, start one. If your church is not large enough to support such an effort, go ecumenical and get several churches to band together. Make the service known at the county marriage license bureaus and the Justices of the Peace and to all ministers in your community. Call larger churches in your area if you do not have a curriculum outline. Some of them will have suggestions you can use.

Then take a look at what your church is doing about marriage enrichment. If it is not more than a once a year event, recommend that resources be created to focus on healthy family groups on a weekly, year-round basis. Make it a priority for your church to take the lead in your community to stop the creation and development of dysfunctional families, and let's go rescue some of those who are already foundering. Don't wait for someone else to start. Take the initiative. Put this book down and make the first call. Do it right now.

6. Analyze and evaluate the media and entertainment offerings that are in your home. Listen to the lyrics of your children's music. Look closely at the video games they play. Watch prime-time television and movies and count the instances where dysfunction is displayed as "normal." Make a conscious family decision about the messages you want to send to each other by the subtle and insidious offerings that we have so often taken for granted. Write letters to the editor. Turn off the television. Contact movie, TV and music producers and express your concerns. Get your friends to do the same. Good stuff doesn't have to be dysfunctional or full of violence or foul language or nudity or overt sex.

7. The final hurdle is getting enough help to those who need and will take it. There are not enough trustworthy therapists. There is not enough insurance coverage. There are far too many people who cannot afford hundreds of dollars in fees to get mentally and emotionally healthy in their homes and families. There are lots of print and video and audio resources available nearly everywhere. Start small groups. Build standards of conduct and hold each other accountable. Be a mentor for a family who is not as far along the journey as yours is. Teach what you know. But, for now, start something. Make like a turtle and stick your neck out.

As Zig Ziglar is often quoted, "If you help enough other people get what they want, you will get what you want."

There may not be another day if we don't seize this one. If we lose our ability to create a healthy society populated by healthy families raising healthy children, let's don't lose without a fight. Let's go out with a bang, not a whimper. I believe that we can change our currents trends in a single generation. I'm in, how about you?

183

About the Author

Don Richard "Dick" Ivey, Ph.D. had a promising career in church administration and university teaching cut short in the early 1970s when he and his original wife dissolved their marriage, leaving two small boys to struggle with the uncertainties of being single-parented by both their parents. Adding insult to injury, the large church where he was employed asked him to resign.

Suddenly, he was without marriage, home, children, vocation, job and job search skills. The pain of that much unaccustomed loss produced a forty pound weight loss and a deep sense of embarrassment.

Survival issues became urgent and he had limited tools. Simple, taken-for-granted, things became Everest-like: finding a place to live, getting enough to eat, finding a job, absentee-parenting two young sons, rebuilding self-esteem.

Negative self talk said, "How could a smart rat like you come to such a lousy end? You are well educated, younger than most of your contemporaries vocationally by at least ten years, handsome, personable....but you don't have enough sense to come in from the rain when it comes to husbanding and daddying. Why not?" The hurt was almost unbearable.

Dick Ivey started looking for resources that people preparing to become husbands and wives and parents could use to prepare. It was a shock to discover that he was not unique. We live in a society that values spending more time and money on weddings than on marriages. There is no "marriage school." Our social order even deifies "on the job training." If a candidate can find someone to say "yes" and can afford the price of a license, our society assumes readiness for marriage and family.

In the early '80s, Ivey became obsessed with the notion that we are never going to change for the better the social ills of our society unless we first create stronger, healthier, more committed families into which to birth and rear healthy children. There was no one out there with enough voice and influence to bring that about. That was when the idea of KenField Institute (KFI) was born.

Since those days, Dick Ivey has devoted much of his discretionary time to the fulfillment of the dream that KFI will become....an independently endowed think-tank focusing on family issues from the vantage point of government, business and industry, education, religion, media and entertainment, and healthcare delivery issues.

Acquiring endowment to ensure the uninterrupted and independent work of KFI takes a great deal of time to amass. Dr. Ivey and his bride, Barbara, have a commitment to help families change and grow new skills and deepen commitments--and, until they can do so on a large scale, will continue to share what they have learned, one family at a time.

The Iveys have counseled lots of couples contemplating marriage. They have officiated at many of their weddings. In each case, advance preparation is coupled with a signed commitment from the brides and grooms that they will seek help when needed, and that they cannot contemplate calling in lawyers without calling the Iveys first for some first-aid and maybe some second and third-aid as well. Raising healthy families is hard work, and whether globally or simply one at a time, Dr. and Mrs. Ivey are making a difference.

Ivey is a B.A. graduate of Howard Payne University, Brownwood, Texas, and also holds the M.R.E./M.A. and Ed.D. /Ph.D. degrees from Southwestern Baptist Theological Seminary, Ft. Worth, Texas.

During seminary days, Dr. Ivey worked as Minister of Education/ Administration in churches in Texas and Oklahoma, and also taught at Oklahoma Baptist University, Shawnee, Oklahoma and his own alma mater, Howard Payne University.

When his original marriage failed, Dr. Ivey began an entrepreneurial odyssey spanning a quarter century.

The crack of dawn of the 1990s produced back-to-back business failures. Massive collapses in banking, real estate, and oil and gas in Texas extracted a serious toll. Dick Ivey was out of work and broke--again. It was like *deja vu* from the middle 1970s--all over again.

He was introduced by a friend to a fledgling telecommunications company in Dallas, Texas, whom he pestered for a sales job for nearly four months. Even though told repeatedly that he did not have the expertise or experience to do the job, his persistence finally wore the hiring authority down and he began carrying a bag on the street selling telecommunications services.

The fledgling company grew to be acquired by AT&T. Dr. Ivey served the company as an Account Executive, Sales Manager, and eventually Vice President/General Manager for the State of Texas.

While at AT&T, Dr. Ivey volunteered as a Jr. Achievement teacher at an inner city high school. He developed an applied economics curriculum that is the basis for the Practical-Life Curriculum offered by KenField Institute.

Dick and Barbara Ivey were married in 1988, and collectively have three children, two boys and a girl. The children are all married. There are five grandchildren--all boys so far. The senior Iveys officiated at the weddings of all their children.

They live in a Dallas suburb with their last remaining "child" at home, Andrew Piaget, a red toy poodle. Andy is an expensive-watch.....dog.

The KenField Manifesto
Families Matter!

PROGRAM DEVELOPMENT OUTLINE

Dallas, Texas

DICK & BARBARA IVEY

January, 1988

Revised—November 9, 1994

Thesis: *Values and practices that make it possible for society to maintain social order are slowly but inexorably being eroded generation after generation. This condition continues to produce more dysfunctional families as each new generation arrives.*

CURRENT SITUATION

It is impossible to pick up a newspaper without seeing headlines in large bold print rampant with violent crime, growing drug trafficking and abuse, a spreading epidemic of AIDS, gang warfare, weapons in the hands of school children, burgeoning pornography, widespread alcohol abuse, scandals in the delivery of mental health services, increasing incidence of single parent homes and latch key kids, child and spousal abuse and on and on.

The Texas Governor's Commission for Women recently surveyed one hundred twenty community organizations about their chief concerns. The top three concerns were crime, adolescent issues and children's issues.

In nineteen ninety-one President Bush appointed an eight member bipartisan National Commission on America's Urban Families. Former Mayor Annette Strauss of Dallas was co-chair of the commission. The studies by the commission concluded that the most pressing problems plaguing America's cities are poverty, crime, drugs, and teenage pregnancy—all of which are impacted by the breakdown of the family.

Mayor Strauss was quoted in the *Dallas Morning News,* (February twenty-two, nineteen ninety-four) after a nationwide fact finding tour: "What we found is that it is a bad situation that is getting worse. Drugs, crime, gang activity—it can all be blamed on the breakdown of the nuclear family. Something has got to change. I want to see things happen."

Strauss' Commission stated that the most important finding is that children are better off in two-parent homes and that broken homes are the root of many of society's ills.

The report of the Commission was presented to the Bush administration in its closing days under the title *Families First.* Tragically the Clinton administration has yet to formally acknowledge the report or contact commission members.

The Commission's findings included:
- Only six of ten children live with their biological married parents.
- The percentage of children living in single-parent homes has nearly tripled in the last thirty years from nine percent to more than twenty-five percent. In some cities the rates are even higher—Detroit, fifty-five percent; Atlanta, forty-nine percent and Dallas, thirty percent. In ninety percent of these homes, the single-parent family means that there is no father present.
- The percentage of children born to unmarried parents has skyrocketed by more than four hundred percent in the same three decades.
- Two thirds of all children under the age of six years who live in single-parent homes also live in poverty.
- From nineteen sixty to nineteen ninety poor single-parent families increased from twenty-four to more than fifty-three percent.
- More disturbing than the statistics is a tour of any neighborhood that is beset with crime, violence, drugs and poverty.

The Commission's recommendations included:

Overall goals: Empower the family, strengthen marriage, strengthen the relationship between parents and children, build community support for families, change the nation's culture to give families priority.

Recommendations:

- Establish greater tax fairness for families.
- Redesign the welfare system, including limiting dependency to two years, requiring all recipients to work, and requiring unmarried teen mothers to live with their parents instead of establishing separate single-parent households.
- Increase parental authority in education, including respecting parental judgment on sex education curriculum.
- Direct sex education curriculum to stress abstinence as the best protection against unwanted pregnancy and sexually transmitted disease.
- Foster enduring, stable marriages through premarital counseling and the establishment of an income tax deduction for couples who complete counseling. Employers could also make marriage counseling an employee benefit.
- Change workplace policies to increase parental time with children, including job-protected leave for a new baby, flexible working hours and more job-sharing and part-time opportunities.
- Identify the father of every child born in the country and strengthen the enforcement of child support payments by non-custodial parents.
- Change television content to support family values, including creating technology that allows parents to block reception of certain channels and programs.
- Establish a presidential advisory council to monitor progress on strengthening family life and serve as a clearinghouse for information sharing on effective community programs that support families.

Despite the Commission's report, local school boards across the country, attempting to address moral values are repeatedly met with opposition by

191

those whose children are most at risk from the erosion of those values. School boards that do take stands in favor of values are often dismissed as being part of the *Radical* or *Religious Right*. The problem has become systemic.

The prevailing sentiment among many people is that the home and the church are the places these values should be taught, not in the schools. The record speaks for itself. Neither the home nor the church nor the school has done a particularly good job in imparting these values in any observable and meaningful way. So, whose job is it?

It is the contention of the KenField Institute that we will not seriously begin to correct these ills in our society or capture the values that many prize until we begin to build better people to populate our communities. We will not begin to build better people until we build better families in which people are raised. We will not begin to build better families until we begin to understand that better families do not happen by accident or by some osmotic process. No child is born with a propensity for violence, crime or addiction unless that predisposition is imprinted by parental genetics or cultural environment. We can affect both influences.

There is virtually no evidence that we are better, kinder, gentler, more sensitive and better equipped for successful living this generation than we were in the past. Likewise, there is no encouragement that the next generation will be better than the current one.

One definition of insanity is doing the same things the same old ways expecting a different result. If we intend to preserve a meaningful society, we must stop the trend to violence, crime, dysfunction and immorality that increasingly and exponentially plagues our nation.

THE NEED

In recent years Senator Jay Rockefeller, Democrat from West Virginia, introduced an omnibus Senate bill on children with a price tag of fifty-four billion, which addressed everything from healthcare to daycare to child abuse to education and after school care. The focus of this bill was reactive and not proactive. Hardly a dollar was earmarked for preventive measures to help our society grow a new generation of healthy families and children. Virtually all the focuses of the bill were upon rescuing those who have already washed over the dam, or fallen off the cliff.

The question that begs asking is, 'When are we going to stop running an ambulance service at the bottom of the valley and go back up the hill to build fences to keep others from falling off?'

A FENCE OR AN AMBULANCE

Twas a dangerous cliff as they freely confessed,
though to walk near its crest was so pleasant;
but over its terrible edge there had slipped a Duke
and many a peasant.

Some people said something would have to be done,
but their projects did not all tally,
some said, 'Put a fence around the edge of the cliff,'
some, 'An ambulance down in the valley.'

But the cry for the ambulance carried the day,
for it spread through the neighboring city,
a fence may be useful or not it's true,
but each heart became brimful of pity.

For those who slipped over that dangerous cliff,
and the dwellers in highway and alley
gave pounds or gave pence, not to put up a fence,
but an ambulance down in the valley.

'For the cliff is all right if you're careful,' they said,
'and if folks even slip and are dropping,
it isn't the slipping that hurts them so much
as the shock down below when they're stopping.'

193

So day after day when those mishaps occurred,
quick forth would these rescuers rally
to pick up the victims who fell off the cliff
with their ambulance down in the valley.

Then an old sage remarked, 'It's a marvel to me
that people give far more attention
to repairing results than to stopping the cause,
when they'd much better aim at prevention.

'Let us stop at its source all the mischief,' cried he
'Come, neighbors and friends, let us rally,
if the cliff we will fence we might almost dispense
with the ambulance down in the valley.'

'Oh, he's a fanatic,' the others rejoined,
'Dispense with the ambulance? Never!
'He'd dispense with all charities, too, if he could'
No! No! we'll support them forever.

Aren't we picking up folks just as fast as they fall?
and shall this man dictate to us? Shall he?
why should people of sense stop to put up a fence
while the ambulance works in the valley?'

But a sensible few who are practical too,
will not bear with such nonsense much longer,
they believe that prevention is better than cure
and their party will soon be the stronger.

Encourage them then, with your purse, voice and pen,
and while other philanthropists dally,

194

they will scorn all pretense and put up a stout fence
on the cliff that hangs over the valley.

Better guide well the young than reclaim them when old,
for the voice of true wisdom is calling,
'To rescue the fallen is good, but it's best
to prevent other people from falling.'

Better close up the source of temptation and crime
deliver from dungeon or galley,
better put a strong fence round the top of the cliff
than an ambulance down in the valley. — *Joseph Malins*

Religion, morality and ethics do not define this issue. It is about *what works* and *does not, what works well* and *what works best.* The ultimate answers will take the best efforts of our most creative minds in **education, religion, government, media and entertainment, business and industry and healthcare delivery.**

THE RESOURCES

A cursory review of the literature and organizations that influence family living for the better reveals a plethora of small tightly focused organizations, programs and individuals who have a piece of the answer to the problem.

Several think tanks focus energies on family values and practices.

A catalog file is constantly being updated.

Numerous directories list resources that are and can be directed toward changing family knowledge and practice.

On-line databases offer additional resources and forums for family value education and improvement.

A sampling of active programs reveals that there are pockets of work in many quarters directed toward family education, values and wholeness, but nothing that has captured the imagination of and resources of our entire society.

From whence then will come the leadership motivation to mount a national initiative? Perhaps a catalyst force will emerge to gather the pieces into a unified whole or perhaps some well organized and independently funded organization will emerge to focus the attention of our nation on the significant opportunity to stop the trends and start building functional families in the new century. That is *the focus* of KenField Institute. That is *the gap* KenField Institute means to fill.

STATEMENT OF WORK

KenField Institute is a private foundation for research, influence, program development and implementation of programs and procedures designed to change for the better the ways we "conduct" family living in the United States.

The Institute operates in six directorates: **Education, Government, Religion, Business and Industry, Media and Entertainment, and Healthcare Delivery Systems.**

EDUCATION DIRECTORATE

Let's begin with a cursory look at the American system of education and how it might be successfully modified to help stem the tide. Very little in the orderly course of education in the American system prepares anyone to be a mature responsible adult. Virtually everyone who becomes a functional adult does so only after consciously deciding to learn and live in a constant state of discovery. Some do not acquire functional skills until "natural" responses produce painful failures. Many, maybe most, never grow up.

In family life, frequently more time and money are spent on weddings than on marriages. Few are prepared to be marriage partners when they say, "I do."

What would happen if we reordered the priorities of education? *What if* we began with a serious commitment to teach young children to, first and foremost, read—then to write, to calculate, to operate computers and to type? Armed with these skills, students can master any subject essential to a balanced education—history, language arts, literature, government, economics, math, science and social studies.

What if, beyond these basics, we agreed to include specific preparations at every level of instruction on how to become successful adults?

What if we taught them *how to* practice etiquette, politeness, table manners and other graces; *when to* use please, thank you, you're welcome, may I and excuse me?

And, *what if we taught* social graces, chivalry and written acknowledgments of gifts; *when to* stand and sit in mixed company; and *the basics of* proper posture, eye contact, handshake and business etiquette?

What if we taught kids *how to* have honor, integrity and commitment to speaking truth; respect for patriotism; and elimination of situational ethics?

What if we taught them the *how to* rules on personal improvement such as hygiene, fashion, hair-care, skincare and fashion for school, play and work; along with nutrition and fitness?

What if we taught them *how to* stretch their imaginations, set goals, cope with the symptoms and causes of codependency, make lists of things to do before dying, make visual dream boards, learn time management skills and acquire the tools necessary to study causes and cures of codependency?

What if we taught them *how to* resolve conflict, that not all conflict is bad, that conflict in relationships is evidence that something needs attention? And, just suppose that in studying the art of compromise they learned that conflict resolution and relationships are much more important than any opinion or position.

What if they could master Harville Hendrix's "container exercise"— *Getting the Love You Want* to manage rage?

What if we taught them *how to* communicate effectively, to develop their written and verbal communication skills, to learn to ask for what they want and not expect intimate associates to read their mind or guess what they want?

What if their skills included dialogue, active listening and a commitment to hear and be heard?

What if we taught them *how to* produce quality work and to be able to prize it, to have a commitment to excellence and quality principles?

What if we taught them the *how to* of dating etiquette, *the appropriate age* to begin dating, *how to* ask for dates, *where to* go on dates, *appropriate behavior* on dates, *how to* end a date and *how to* assist youth and parents to set responsible community dating standards?

What if we taught *how to* sex education that honors abstinence, the importance of caring, the value of respect for self and others, the dignity of choosing to wait, the setting of boundaries in advance and that not all sexual choices are equal?

What if we taught the consequences of premarital sex, about physiology and sexually transmitted disease, the tragedy of babies having babies and about eliminating pressures to perform sexually?

What if we taught *how to* select a mate and why most people choose a mate that has the same bad traits as their own parents?

What if we taught the chemistry of romantic selection, *how to* plan a marriage and not just a wedding, *how to* understand the imperative of commitment and that all marriage skills are learned and have nothing to do with emotional attraction?

What if we taught *how to* get education beyond public school, making a choice between college, trade or a military education, about financial resources available for higher education, preparation for acceptance and how to secure grants, scholarships, and work opportunities?

What if we taught *how to* look for a job or career and to analyze dreams, interests, aptitudes and gifts?

And, *what if* we taught *where to* look for a job, *whom to look to* for help, *how to* network, dress, speak and follow up in order to be remembered?

What if we taught *how to* fill out a job application, the advantage of taking a sample application with their history written out as a guide, *how to* deal with the gatekeeper, to print not write, *what to* include and *what to* omit, to bring their own pen to an interview and *how to* follow up?

What if we taught *how to* write a resume—style, content, grabbing and holding the attention of the prospective employer in the first ten seconds, results reporting and telling the truth?

What if we taught *how to* get a job interview—from the telephone request to managing the gatekeeper to refusing to take "no" for an answer?

What if we taught *how to* conduct job interviews—handling the two interviews that occur at the same time (i.e. interviewing the interviewer while he or she is interviewing you), preparation and company knowledge, *how to* dress, posture, what to take, questions to expect and to ask, *how to* use effective pauses, closing questions and follow up?

What if we taught *how to* get rich before you die—the magic of compound interest, time plus discipline equal wealth; how anyone can retire a millionaire on two dollars and seventy-four cents a day? It can happen.

What if we taught *how to* manage finances—budgeting, banking, record keeping, discretionary spending and big expenditures?

What if we taught *how to* buy cars and never have car payments, the burden of negative compound interest, paying for a car, driving it three to five more years while saving payments for the ultimate cash purchase of new car—and to continue the practice throughout one's lifetime?

What if we taught *how to* buy homes—whether to buy or rent, choosing the right location, learning about realtors, mortgages, title companies and attorneys work; and the secrets of delayed satisfaction?

What if we taught *how to* invest wisely—investment commitment, how much, markets, full service and discount brokers, Internet investing, fees, yields, dividends and retirement planning programs?

What if we taught *how to* establish banking and credit relationships—shopping for a banker, relationships with bank officers, where and how to establish credit, the onerous lies of credit card companies and building a credit strategy that minimizes the disastrous impact of negative compound interest?

What if we taught *how to* budget—tools needed, commitment to the process, how much to allocate for each category and living below your means?

What if we taught *how to* estate plan—where to find help, making a will, setting priorities and starting with the end in view?

What if we taught *how to* shop for consumables—to buy what you want and never pay retail, the value of coupon shopping, the art of negotiation and bargain hunting?

What if we taught *how to* account for resources without being a certified public accountant—a commitment to keep records, receipts and decisions on the division of responsibility?

What if we taught *how to* manage taxes and insurance needs—whether to hire a specialist or prepare your own income tax forms, the *why* of insurance and how much and what kind of life, health, car, home or renters insurance one should maintain?

What if we taught *how to* establish a home, how it is more than a house—and how to define the roles of participants and practice the art of family and home?

What if we taught *how to* decide to start a family responsibly—when to start it, how many children to have, how far apart should children be spaced and birth control practices?

What if we taught *how to* rear functional children, where to go for help, the importance of the first three years, avoiding the dangers of codependency, how spending time together is the best gift and how to build traditions?

What if we taught *how to* preserve marriages—keeping the romance alive, remembering special days, practicing the art of intimacy, learning to communicate and the value of commitment/intentional marriage?

What if we taught *how to* be successful wives and husbands—defining the roles, equalitarian roles, communicating and meeting each other's needs?

What if we taught *how to* develop successful use of leisure time—developing things to do together, retaining things to do individually, planning vacations and holidays, ways to avoid falling victim to parental guilt trips, planning weekly dates, consideration of monthly overnight dates and long weekends away quarterly?

What if we taught *how to* accept civic and social responsibility—registering to vote, participation in parent-teacher organizations, selection of community causes to support, contributing to local charities, volunteering and making lists of local, state and national opportunities?

What if we taught *how to* make informed religious decisions—the mental health value of spiritual commitment, evaluation of options and involvement in organized spiritual activities with an open mind?

What if we taught *how to* deal with aging parents—increased longevity after retirement, treating diseases related to aging, inadequate retirement provisions, living arrangements for aging parents and parents who require long term medical care?

What if we taught *how to* plan for retirement—social security, retirement programs, personal investments, company retirement benefits, how much is enough, where and when to retire and meaningful things to do in retirement?

What if we taught *how to* cope with death and dying—the death of loved ones, spiritual implications, funeral planning and arrangements, counseling and other aspects?

Why is it not just as important to teach children how to be grownups as it is to teach them how to recite multiplication tables and diagram sentences? If we teach a generation of children and their parents how to be better wives, husbands and parents, is it possible we will raise better subsequent generations of children? If we raise better subsequent generations of children, is it possible that some—perhaps many—of the social problems we face will be moderated?

The hue and cry these days is away from federally mandated control and for more local control of these issues. On the other hand school districts that have attempted to interject these values have been greeted none too warmly by parents who insist that these issues should best be left to home and church.

Unfortunately the track record of both home and church has not created massive numbers of informed and well-prepared adults. As important as other institutions are in creating change, education must take advantage of its captive audience and make these practical applications part of the subject matter it uses to create and polish the skills of reading, writing, calculating and computing.

What then are recommendations that need to be explored, researched, packaged, tested and sold for implementation to the American education system by KenField Institute?

1. Keep the Federal government out of local education, except for the setting of standards for the development of functional family education. The people responsible for the postal service and failed savings and loans are not the best choice for packaging and implementing educational reform. Start small and enlist teacher after teacher, school after school, district after district and state after state until genuine practical reform is implemented. Pilot programs to be created and schools enlisted to participate. Statistical records of performance to be kept to determine the efficacy of what is explored.

2. Encourage curricular development to proceed along traditional *developmental task* based tracks.

3. Require more parental involvement in the education of children. Revive procedures that reward participating parents who team with teachers in the education of their children.

4. Develop strategies for increasing local spending commitments to education, including, but not limited to better facilities, year-round school, longer school days, higher teacher salaries and benefits. In addition provide state-of-the-art electronic media (computers with CD-ROM, modems, internet access, interactive videodiscs, networks, distance learning opportunities, integrated learning systems, database accessibility, cable and VCR/videotape and creative software applications). It is hard enough to create a learning environment in settings where teachers have to motivate Nintendo kids with Guttenberg-like tools.

5. Create and promote other programs to teach *how to* skills that are modeled after the Junior Achievement programs of *Applied Economics* that are taught by community volunteers to junior high and high school economics classes.

6. Task the KenField Institute's Education Directorate with the research and development required. Clearly the target is to capture the hearts and minds of the current generation and to create an environment in which future generations will view the improvements we make on purpose as the standard for educational activity.

The task is monumental and must address education at home and at all school levels. The KenField Institute views this task as a journey and not a destination. The loss of vigilance in any generation will only start the inexorable slide backwards...again.

Education alone is not the answer. Government, business and industry, media and entertainment, religion and healthcare delivery systems must also contribute in order to build a society of healthy families and eliminate crime, violence, drugs, gangs, and all the other dysfunctional activity that plagues the nation.

GOVERNMENT DIRECTORATE
While federal and state government pay lip service to providing services to families, most services are entitlement programs to support families that are already in crisis. The motivation to move away from such programs is not inherent in those who provide the services. Serious changes in current practices will prove to be job threatening to thousands of persons who make their living delivering welfare, entitlement and crisis services to families.

A cursory review of current practices pits the conservative rhetoric for reform and reduction of welfare against the clamor of the champions of entitlement to expand services.

Several things are apparent. Governments do not require any preparation to be licensed to be married or to be a parent. While requiring stringent requirements to be licensed for everything from driving a car to serving in professional capacities, the laws of the land are strangely silent about licensing marriages and families.

What if we reordered the priorities of government regarding families and required some preparation work in order to be married or training procedures in order to be a parent?

What if we offered incentives to families who perform healthily, such as first year tax incentives for first-time newly married people who do certain testing and preparation work and tax breaks for people who stay married more than twenty-five years to the same person.

What if we required the recommendations of the President's Commission on Urban Families to become law? For example, identify the fathers of all babies and encourage welfare recipients to keep fathers in the home—and limit welfare to a specific number of children and a specific time period for benefits.

What if the government developed incentive programs to both identify and reward quality families?

What if government mandated changes and provided incentives to other segments of society to make family friendly practices the norm rather than the exception?

The task of the Government Directorate will be to identify areas where federal, state and local governments can enact legislation that will enhance the focus on quality families. Much of the focus will be upon items that do not require huge infrastructure support or large financial commitments. The thesis of this directorate's mandate is that the creation of a large number of high quality families will decrease, rather than increase, government resources required to control and contain the social problems that are today fought largely through government spending and taxation.

BUSINESS AND INDUSTRY DIRECTORATE

What if business and industry were to assess the impact on productivity and profitability of family dysfunction? Studies already indicate that absenteeism, shoddy work, decreased attention to quality and detail, increased scrap rates and other profit limiting results come in direct proportion to the stability and quality of the family life of the workers who produce.

The Business and Industry Directorate will enlist a cross section of large and small businesses to participate in research to identify the cost of waste that can be attributed directly or indirectly to family issues out of control. The results of this research will be used to develop and implement procedures and programs that businesses can employ to impact the negative influences in the workplace that stem from poor family practices.

Many corporations today offer EAS (Employee Assistance Services) programs for families in trouble, but they are primarily prescriptive and not preventive programs. The Business and Industry Directorate will quantify the need, design pilot programs and test the hypothesis that companies can do family friendly things that will increase productivity and give greater attention to quality in the workplace. Examples of such programs include onsite daycare, flexible working schedules, kids day at work, recognition of wedding anniversaries with an extra vacation day and economic recognition of those married to the same person for milestone periods. Other examples include family outings, support groups, mandatory family seminars, learning experiences for employees whose families are not in trouble, mentoring programs and telecommuting.

Successful programs will be packaged and made available to other companies with encouragement to reinvest part of the money they save from applying of such programs to create other family friendly initiatives and to enlist other companies to join in or cooperate in similar programs. Healthier families and healthier companies where they work will add another component to radical change in the quality of family life in this country.

MEDIA AND ENTERTAINMENT DIRECTORATE

Perhaps the most difficult directorate to staff and develop will focus on media and entertainment. There are numerous reasons. Primarily, media tend to be more liberal than not. First Amendment rights are always employed to defend whatever the alleged *artistic* mind can create (regardless of its functionality). Our culture has become progressively more accepting of voyeurism. Very few standards of decency and propriety characterize the industry and there is no observable sense of responsibility for shaping the minds and behavior of society in the majority of media/entertainment offerings available.

In music, video, television, movies, print entertainment, radio, talk shows, tabloid journalism and the private lives of many that *star* in these mediums, the tendency of our culture is to showcase the seamiest sides of life. With the throwaway cliché that *we don't make standards, we just reflect them*, producers in media and entertainment have consistently taken the lowest roads looking for what sells.

Generation after generation has been desensitized to the gradual slide away from such character traits as modesty, fidelity, monogamy, sexual abstinence outside marriage, functional families, integrity, honesty, virtue and commitment. In their place, we have substituted glitzy packages promising things that simply cannot deliver what they advertise: immodesty, nudity, infidelity, sexual license, families out of control, honesty and integrity for a price and commitment that lasts only until it is inconvenient.

The current situation did not arrive full-grown. The healing process will not occur overnight. This directorate will research and quantify the impact of the backward slide of family values on cultural stability and then craft long range strategies to stop the current trends and begin to reverse the process.

This directorate will persuade media and producers of entertainment to do the extra work necessary to deliver wares that do not run away from the highest standards as though they are somehow beneath the erudite sophisticates of our society. The Media and Entertainment Directorate may create a *KenField Seal of Approval* endorsement for media offerings much like the *UL* label and *Good Housekeeping Seal of Approval.*

RELIGION DIRECTORATE

Although religion is generally charged with the mandate of being the social and moral conscience of our society, the impact of religion on the behavior of our society has been anything but stellar.

Numerous national surveys about religion indicate that the vast majority of people in our culture believe in God, but that such belief has little, if any, impact on how they live. Only a fraction of our citizens have anything to do with organized religion.

The Religion Directorate will not try to enlist persons to participate in any particular religion, but will be charged with the research and development of universal strategies that will enable churches, mosques and synagogues to better prepare people for family roles in the twenty-first century.

Parenthetically it is the contention of KenField Institute that the message of religion will find more fertile grounds for acceptance in the lives of persons who take seriously the demands of learning and practicing family skills that work and work well. The distractions of dysfunction must not be permitted to remain a continuing inhibition to the expansion of religious faith and practice.

Emphases, programs, resources and cooperative efforts will be developed for the purpose of assisting religious institutions to be more proactive in what they do best—premarital preparation, support groups, religious marriage ceremonies, congenial social groupings, children's education, instruction in values and upholding high ethical standards.

Exploration of meaningful ways in which religion can become a warrior-partner in the fight to produce quality families will be offered to any and all organized religious bodies who are willing to participate. A clearinghouse of resources—human, print, video, electronic, home study, interactive and other will be sought out, created and made available.

The Religion Directorate will begin with an examination of families that work well and families that are in crisis to discover if there is a common component of faith and practice in either or both. Inferences will be drawn from the results of such research and used to make recommendations about the impact of religion on the quality of family life.

HEALTHCARE DELIVERY SYSTEMS

The Healthcare Delivery Systems Directorate has frequently been viewed as an anomaly in the KenField Family. In some respects the most significant task of all may be assigned to this directorate.

Anyone with group medical coverage has seen the erosion of mental and emotional healthcare benefits by third party providers.

In past years it was not uncommon to find healthcare providers that provided both inpatient and outpatient care at meaningful levels. Today it is common to find that coverage has been reduced by more than fifty percent. Limitations have been set on the time available for inpatient medical reimbursement as well as outpatient services. The trend is away from providing insurance benefits for mental and emotional healthcare. Risk/reward analysts for insurance companies have determined that needs are so great and costs so high that meaningful coverage cannot be afforded by the general public.

It is increasingly apparent that families that do not have personal wealth or extraordinary medical coverage cannot receive quality mental and emotional healthcare. Few people can afford fifty to one hundred twenty-five dollars per hour outpatient, or five hundred to one thousand dollars per day inpatient.

The monumental task of this directorate is to find ways to make mental and emotional healthcare services readily and universally available. This directorate will catalog public and private resources, explore and recommend alternatives, develop greater self-help resources, maximize other institutional resources such as education and church, consider mentoring programs for community-wide support, develop community based interactive media resources and hot-line audio and video programs for example.

The goal is to produce adequate resources for the delivery of real time, all time health care to those who need it.

ANCILLARY SUPPORT SERVICES

The six directorates will be supported by six support services focusing on the directorate issues from the vantage point of men's issues, women's issues, youth issues, children's issues, minority issues and legal issues. Each support service will address the issues of each directorate from its particular gender, ethnic and/or legal perspective. The ultimate compilation of recommendations and offerings will be reviewed from all sides and viewpoints to create the clearest strategies for success.

KFI will also construct a conference/residential educational center for the target groups to whom the KenField Institute focuses its services: premarital couples, developing families who desire better marriages, dysfunctional marriages and families, codependents, corporate executives and representatives of all six directorates. The center will also be an empirical testing ground for plans and programs developed by the institute.

LAUNCH STRATEGY FOCUS GROUP PLANNING

The subcommittees of the Founding Directors of KenField will schedule the first two years of work. Three focus groups will concentrate their attention on **Facilities, Program** and **Personnel** requirements and be chaired by the VP/Operations-(**Facilities**), the CEO/President and the Executive VP/Administration-(**Program**) and the Sr. VP/CFO-(**Personnel**).

Creative options that will be considered by the leadership of the directorates include, but are not limited to:

■ The establishment of an international clearinghouse for Family Service providers and programs,

■ Annual Nobel-like Prizes for exemplary programs and researchers,

■ Pilot projects ,

■ Processes and procedures for identifying worthy service providers and programs to whom to make grants,

■ The development of a "skunkworks" approach of give-and-take to create the most productive and synergistic atmosphere in which the Directorate staffs and Support Service staffs will work.

FINANCIAL RESOURCES REQUIRED

Facilities to house KFI offices will include a fifty to seventy-five room hotel, healthcare clinic, IPC (Information Processing Center), amphitheater and multimedia teaching center and ancillary support services. The IPC will be

equipped with state-of-the-art information gathering equipment including, but not limited to: fiber optic connections to local and long distance
voice and data networks, satellite up link, digital cellular, high speed
internet access and mega data storage and retrieval systems. KFI will be
connected to all significant databases in the nation. One hundred to two
hundred acres, perhaps on the campus of a country club, will be acquired.

KFI will purchase Millhurst Farms in East Texas for construction
of The Center. It will be developed to accommodate at least a hundred
clients/guests at a time.

KFI will purchase Oak Lake Ranch and, if available, the rights to
Koinonia Lodge for a family Retreat Center.

Sufficient endowment will be acquired to enable a five percent
annual distribution to sustain personnel, programs, satellite offices, The
Center and all operating costs in perpetuity. Approximately two billion
eight hundred million dollars will be required for permanent endowment funding. Another four hundred million dollars in initial capital
will be required for all purchases, construction and the first year's operations. This will enable the work of KenField to continue in perpetuity.

Although KenField will win many battles, the war will never be
won. Vigilance over families must continue forever unabated. This endowment will enable KenField to be a watchdog for families until the end
of the world. The magnitude of this vision will preclude anyone from claiming credit for its success. Only the intervention of Divine Providence
can provide resources like these for families.

STATEMENT OF MISSION

KenField Institute will be the premier research, development and promotion organization in the world championing family issues.

KFI will build a team that will become the most respected name in
family life issues in the world, attract and keep a team of the most outstanding people available, create and maintain an atmosphere of mutual
trust and respect and listen to the people who do the work.

A primary emphasis will be the personal and professional development of team members. KFI will:

- Have only one class of team member. Each member will be a full partner.
- Recognize and reward excellence while the individual is still sweating from his efforts.
- Build and maintain a spirit of *one for all and all for one.*
- Encourage every team member to care more than others think is wise, risk more than others think is safe, dream more than others think is practical, expect more than others think is possible, make decisions, exercise initiative and never be afraid to make mistakes.
- Hold team members accountable for results. Team members will be given great flexibility in deciding how to achieve results, with the understanding that ethical standards must never be compromised.
- Eliminate any opportunity for people to succeed by merely *looking good.*

Leaders of the team must live in the field, first feed the troops and then the officers, always lead by example and never ask anyone to do something they would not do.

Each team member will:

- Deliver services of such high quality that it will create even better opportunities for new people joining the team.
- Be available twenty-four hours a day, seven days a week, to go anywhere and do whatever necessary to serve family causes—but strive to maintain a work schedule of four days a week, seven to ten hours a day.
- Conduct their professional and personal lives in a manner that will bring credit to the godly image of *Family* at all times.
- Eliminate bureaucracy wherever it is found within the organization.

The KFI Team will be known for its intense, competitive spirit. It will always compete to:

- Maintain the best competitive win/loss record in the war to preserve and defend *family* values.
- Confront every negative influence to family wholeness—never fearing to take on any segment of society that negatively impacts *the family*—no matter how well established or accepted. It will not be enough to do *just enough to win.*
- Win fairly, equitably and in a manner that establishes the Institute's reputation as the most effective, creative and relentless organization in the world in defense of *the family.*

The ethical standards of team members must, obviously, be impeccable. He or she must model ideal family wholeness behaviors and commit to *doing* the work of maintaining that role in their home.

He or she will accept nothing from suppliers, special interest groups or the government that might compromise their integrity, will do nothing that gives the appearance of impropriety, and will always operate in the center of the field of ethical behavior and prize integrity above all.

KFI will not tolerate acts that bring discredit to the organization. Any member of the team confronted with dysfunction in his or her own family who refuses to do the work of wholeness will be held accountable. The team will not tolerate discrimination against another with regard to race, religion, sex or any other reason; looking down on others; becoming a corporate politician; trying to move ahead at the expense of others; or using illegal drugs.

By the end of our lives we will be the most respected name in family wholeness. Of us it will be said, "They fought the good fight, they finished the course, they kept the faith."

And, finally, we will all have fun participating in a grand adventure—building new families for the twenty-first century and beyond.